WORLD OF VOCABULARY

BLUE

Sidney J. Rauch   Alfred B. Weinstein

Assisted by Muriel Harris

GLOBE BOOK COMPANY, INC.

A Division of Simon & Schuster

New York/Cleveland/Toronto/Sydney/Tokyo/Singapore

PHOTO CREDITS

Page 2, 5, 7, 26, 29, 31, 32, 35, 37, 56, 59, 61, 80, 83, 85, 86, 89, 91, 98, 101, 102, 104, 115: Wide World Photos; 8, 41, 97: UPI/The Bettmann Archive; 11, 79: Photofest; 13, 38, 43: Smeal/Galella Ltd.; 14, 19: Alice Waters/Chez Panisse; 17: Deanne Fitzmaurice/San Francisco Chronicle; 20: Program Corporation of America; 23, 24: Marth Swope; 44, 49: Neg. no 334109. Courtesy of Department Library Services American Museum of National History; 47: Francois Gohier/Photo Researchers; 50, 53, 55: Peter Jordan; 62, 65, 67: Frederic Reglain/ Gamma Liaison; 68, 71, 73: Wally Amos; 74, 77, 79: Ron Galella; 92, 95: Leo De Wys; 107, 109: Todd Webb/Courtesy Amon Carter Museum, Fort Worth, Texas; 110, 113: The Bettmann Archive; 116: ICM Artists Limited; 119: Walter H. Scott/Boston Symphony Orchestra; 121: Chris Lee 1989/New York Philharmonic.

World of Vocabulary, Blue Level, Third Edition
Sidney J. Rauch   Alfred B. Weinstein

ISBN 1-55675-366-7

Printed in the United States of America
10 9 8 7

SIDNEY J. RAUCH is Professor of Reading and Education at Hofstra University, and senior author of the World of Vocabulary series. He has been a visiting professor at numerous universities and is active as a lecturer and consultant. As a member of the College Proficiency Examination Committee of the New York State Education Department, he was involved in the certification of reading personnel. He has given in-service courses and has served as consultant to over thirty school districts in New York, Florida, North Carolina, South Carolina, and the U.S. Virgin Islands. Dr. Rauch was named Reading Educator of the Year for 1985 by the New York State Reading Association.

As coauthor and editor, his texts include: A Need to Read series, *Handbook for the Volunteer Tutor (Second Edition), Guiding the Reading Program, Cloze Thinking, Mastering Reading Skills,* and *Corrective Reading in the High School Classroom.* He is author of the Barnaby Brown books, a children's series. Dr. Rauch's many articles have appeared in *The Reading Teacher, Journal of Reading, Reading World,* and conference proceedings of the International Reading Association.

ALFRED B. WEINSTEIN is the former principal of Myra S. Barnes Intermediate School (Staten Island, N.Y.). Dr. Weinstein has taught extensively at the secondary school level, and he has served as an elementary school principal and assistant principal. He has been a reading clinician and instructor at Hofstra University Reading Center. At Queens College he gave courses in reading improvement, and at Brooklyn College he taught in the graduate teacher education program. Dr. Weinstein has also taught reading for the New York City Board of Education's in-service teacher training program. He was head of Unit 1 of the Board of Examiners and supervised the licensing of teachers, supervisors, administrators, psychologists, and social workers for the New York City Board of Education. He is vice-president of the Council of Supervisors and Administrators of Local 1 of the AFL-CIO. Dr. Weinstein has been listed in *Who's Who in the East* since 1982.

Dr. Weinstein is a contributor to the *Handbook for the Volunteer Tutor* and one of the authors of *Achieving Reading Skills.* With Dr. Rauch, he is coauthor of *Mastering Reading Skills.*

MURIEL HARRIS has been an elementary school teacher for twenty-five years. She has taught in-service courses in individualized reading and creative writing, and has designed curricula for those subjects. Mrs. Harris has served as a vice president of the National Council of Teachers of English. Her articles have appeared in *Instructor, Grade Teacher, Elementary English,* and publications of the New York State Teachers' Association magazine. She won the *Nassau Review* 1990 Poetry Award.

CONTENTS ▪▪▪▪▪▪▪▪▪▪▪▪▪▪▪▪▪▪▪▪▪▪▪▪▪▪▪▪▪▪▪▪▪▪

▪▪

1 GOOD AND GOOD FOR YOU

Alice Waters is known to many gourmets as the Queen Mother of California cuisine . She founded one of America's most famous restaurants, Chez Panisse, in Berkeley, California. Waters has done more than any other restauranteur to popularize the belief that food should be both good and good for you.

Most of the produce served at Waters' restaurant is organic . The meat is from animals raised without chemical additives . Both are locally grown to insure freshness.

Formerly a schoolteacher in New Jersey, Alice Waters opened her Berkeley restaurant in 1971. The message of healthy food was clear from the beginning. The culinary revolution she started, however, was one of taste . She led the way, first in California and then nationwide, to the demand for first-quality ingredients, simply prepared. She brought new attention to the excellence of American food. Formerly humble dishes, such as pizza, were changed into fare for serious restaurants.

In an effort to provide organic food to more people, Waters is helping to open a market in Oakland, south of Berkeley. She hopes that increased demand will create competition and lower prices.

Waters thinks people should eat her food "because they think it's wonderful." If it is chemical-free, "the food is pleasing to the senses because it partakes of the essence of the earth."

˜˜˜˜˜˜˜˜˜˜˜ UNDERSTANDING THE STORY ˜˜˜˜˜˜˜˜˜˜˜

▶Circle the letter next to each correct statement.

1. The statement that best expresses the main idea of this selection is:
   a. School teachers from New Jersey should open restaurants in California.
   b. Alice Waters has proved that a good meal must consist of good ingredients and careful preparation.
   c. The most important thing about food is its affect on health.

2. According to the story, you can conclude that
   a. Waters knew what would best suit her principles and her customers' tastes.
   b. the entire country will soon demand organic, additive-free food.
   c. something must be done about all the boring pizza eaten in this country.

3

▶Here are the ten vocabulary words in this lesson. Write them in alphabetical order in the blank spaces below.

| gourmets | popularize | organic | taste | partakes |
| cuisine | produce | additives | humble | essence |

1. _____   6. _____

2. _____   7. _____

3. _____   8. _____

4. _____   9. _____

5. _____   10. _____

▀▀▀▀▀▀▀▀▀ WHAT DO THE WORDS MEAN? ▀▀▀▀▀▀▀▀▀

▶Here are some meanings for the ten vocabulary words in this lesson. Two words have been written beside their meanings. Write the other eight words next to their meanings.

1. ____taste____ a sense of what is good

2. _____ that which makes something what it is

3. _____ fresh fruits and vegetables

4. _____ make popular

5. _____ shares

6. _____ style of cooking

7. _____ grown without synthetic substances

8. _____ people who like and know about good food

9. ____humble____ lowly

10. _____ a substance added to change or improve a natural product

4

▰▰▰▰▰▰▰▰▰▰▰▰ FIND THE ANALOGIES ▰▰▰▰▰▰▰▰▰▰▰▰

▶ In an **analogy,** similar relationships occur between words that are different. For example, *pig* is to *hog* as *car* is to *automobile.* The relationship is that the words mean the same. Here's another analogy: *noisy* is to *quiet* as *short* is to *tall.* In this relationship, the words have opposite meanings. **See if you can complete the following analogies. Circle the correct word or words.**

1. **Humble** is to **low** as **shiny** is to
   a. dull　　　　　**b.** sunny　　　　**c.** hard　　　　**d.** bright

2. **Popularize** is to **squelch** as **enjoy** is to
   a. experience　**b.** observe　　**c.** like　　　　**d.** reject

3. **Essence** is to **unnecessary** as **extra** is to
   a. showy　　　　**b.** joyful　　　**c.** necessary　**d.** peaceful

4. **Partakes** is to **shares** as **observes** is to
   a. ignores　　　**b.** sees　　　　**c.** controls　　**d.** desires

5. **Produce** is to **food** as **kindness** is to
   a. survival　　　**b.** charm　　　**c.** politeness　**d.** rudeness

▰▰▰▰▰▰▰▰▰▰▰▰ USE YOUR OWN WORDS ▰▰▰▰▰▰▰▰▰▰▰▰

▶ **Look at the picture. What words come into your mind other than the ten vocabulary words used in this lesson? Write them on the blank lines below. To help you get started, here are two good words:**

1. _____wholesome_____
2. _____healthful_____
3. _____
4. _____
5. _____
6. _____
7. _____
8. _____
9. _____
10. _____

▶The **possessive** of a word shows that something belongs to it. For example, Bill has a boat; it is *Bill's* boat. To make a possessive of a word that doesn't end in "s," add an apostrophe and an "s" to the word, such as *baker's* bread or my *father's* car. To make a possessive of a word that does end in "s," add an apostrophe only, such as *friends'* bicycles or *ladies'* hats. **Here are ten words from the story. In the blank space next to the word write the correct possessive of the word.**

1. gourmets _____
2. additives _____
3. competition _____
4. Waters _____
5. belief _____

6. anyone _____
7. cuisine _____
8. animals _____
9. freshness _____
10. beginnings _____

wwwwwwwwww COMPLETE THE STORY wwwwwwwwww

▶**Here are the ten vocabulary words for this lesson:**

gourmets	popularize	organic	taste	partakes
cuisine	produce	additives	humble	essence

▶**There are seven blank spaces in the story below. Three vocabulary words have already been used in the story. They are underlined. Use the other seven words to fill in the blank spaces.**

Alice Waters is famous for her preference for _____ fruits and vegetables or meats grown without _____. She has made personal appearances and gives interviews to _____ her views on these matters. There have always been many _____ in California who wanted their food to be safe and healthful as well as delicious. Now, thanks in part to Waters, restaurants all over the country are trying to obtain better _____.

Unlike many health food fanatics, Alice Waters has always insisted on a <u>cuisine</u> in which wonderful flavors and eye-appeal are most important. The food served in her restaurant <u>partakes</u> of the _____ of true flavors. No matter how _____ the ingredients, Alice Waters can find a way to elevate them to a special level. She has good <u>taste</u> and knows how to apply it.

~~~~~~~~~~~~~~~~~~~~~~~~~~ FOR EXTRA CREDIT ~~~~~~~~~~~~~~~~~~~~~~~~~~

Learn More About Cooking

▶On a separate piece of paper or in your notebook, do the three exercises below. Then turn them in to your teacher.

1 Every profession has its own language and special words. Restaurant management is no exception. Some of the words that chefs and restauranteurs must know are *sauce, saute, braise, whisk, simmer, colander.* Can you define any of these words? If not, look them up in a dictionary and use them in sentences.

2 How would you feel if you went to a foreign country and had to eat a new cuisine? What would some of the new foods be? Select another country and try to find some things they eat that you don't or that you eat that they don't. Write a paragraph describing a complete meal you might be served in that country.

3 Can you cook? Have you ever worked in a restaurant? What skills and talents do you need to do either? Talk to someone who works in a restaurant and interview him or her to discover whether the work sounds appealing. In a paragraph write whether or not you would like to learn enough to work in this business. Give the reasons for your decision.

The young woman stood before the curtain in the Palace The-ater in New York City, her head bowed. The frantic applause of the audience brought tears to her eyes. The New York debut of Bette Midler was a tremendous success.

This setting was very different from the gentle, rolling hills of Aiea, a small town near the city of Honolulu, Hawaii, where Bette Midler was born. Bette's aptitude for music and acting led her into her métier , show business. She came to the mainland and became a member of an acting group that performed for children. Later, in order to support herself, Bette worked in the coatroom of a night-club. One day a friend suggested Bette apply for a role in a play. The producers liked Bette and later gave her an important role in a musical called *Fiddler on the Roof.*

Although she started her career as an actress, Bette first became famous as a pop singer. She received ovations for her dynamic stage presence and her renditions of both old and new songs. Later, she decided to return to acting. In *The Rose,* a film about a rock singer, Bette firmly established her credentials as a skillful actress. From there, she progressed to other roles in dramatic and comic films, such as *Ruthless People, Outrageous Fortune,* and *Beaches.* Today, she is one of the most popular actresses in Hollywood.

Critics commend her performances whether they are on the stage or on the screen. Fans the world over clamor for more from Bette Midler.

⠶⠶⠶⠶⠶⠶⠶⠶ UNDERSTANDING THE STORY ⠶⠶⠶⠶⠶⠶⠶⠶

▶ Circle the letter next to each correct statement.

1. The main purpose of this story is to
   a. describe the place where Bette Midler was born.
   b. tell the reader about some of the events in Bette's career.
   c. encourage young singers to imitate Bette's style.

2. From this story, you can conclude that
   a. Bette Midler was born into show business.
   b. Bette never really liked acting on the stage.
   c. luck, talent, and a lot of hard work have all contributed to Bette's success.

►Here are the ten vocabulary words in this lesson. Write them in alphabetical order in the blank spaces below.

frantic	clamor	métier	aptitude	skillful
renditions	commend	ovations	debut	apply

1. _____

2. _____

3. _____

4. _____

5. _____

6. _____

7. _____

8. _____

9. _____

10. _____

►Here are some meanings for the ten vocabulary words in this lesson. Three words have been written beside their meanings. Write the other seven words next to their meanings.

1. _____ wild with excitement; out of control

2. _____ a first appearance before the public

3. _____ natural ability or capacity; talent

4. _____métier_____ life's work; occupation; profession

5. _____ seek a job; ask for work

6. _____ performances or interpretations

7. _____ having ability gained by practice or knowledge; expert

8. _____ovations_____ bursts of loud clapping or cheering; waves of applause

9. _____commend_____ praise; acclaim as worthy of notice

10. _____ demand noisily; loudly call for

10

⣿⣿⣿⣿ COMPLETE THE SENTENCES ⣿⣿⣿⣿

▶ Use the vocabulary words in this lesson to complete the following sentences. Use each word only once. The first one has been done for you.

métier	ovations	apply	skillful	debut
aptitude	renditions	frantic	commend	clamor

1. Standing ___ovations___ are the dream of many young entertainers.

2. Bette realized early on that her _____ would be in the performing arts.

3. Bette's _____ of songs always thrill her audiences.

4. Before Bette made her _____ , she worked small jobs to become known.

5. Many people _____ for each part in a play, but only a few are chosen.

6. There is a _____ search for a replacement when the star of a show gets sick.

7. Bette Midler has a rare _____ for both comedy and song.

8. No one expected the critics to _____ Bette's performance in the move *The Rose*, but they all gave it rave reviews.

9. Bette is _____ at relaxing her audience and making them enjoy themselves.

10. Fans stand and _____ for more at the end of Bette's performances.

⣿⣿⣿⣿ USE YOUR OWN WORDS ⣿⣿⣿⣿

▶ Look at the picture. What words come into your mind other than the ten vocabulary words used in this lesson? Write them on the blank lines below. To help you get started, here are two good words:

1. _____costume_____
2. _____bunny_____
3. _____
4. _____
5. _____
6. _____
7. _____
8. _____
9. _____
10. _____

ᴡᴡᴡᴡᴡᴡ FIND THE SUBJECTS AND PREDICATES ᴡᴡᴡᴡᴡᴡ

▶The **subject** of a sentence names the person, place, or thing that is spoken about. The **predicate** of a sentence is what is said about the subject. For example:

The small boy   <u>went to the football game.</u>

▶*The small boy* is the person the sentence is about, and *went to the football game* is the predicate of the sentence because it tells what the small boy did. **In the following sentences draw one line under the subject of the sentence and two lines under the predicate of the sentence.**

1. The young woman stood before the curtain.

2. Bette Midler was born in Aiea, Hawaii.

3. Bette became famous as a singer.

4. Critics commend all Bette's performances.

5. Bette performs on the stage and screen.

ᴡᴡᴡᴡᴡᴡᴡᴡᴡᴡ COMPLETE THE STORY ᴡᴡᴡᴡᴡᴡᴡᴡᴡᴡᴡ

▶Here are the ten vocabulary words for this lesson:

frantic	debut	aptitude	métier	renditions
apply	clamor	skillful	commend	ovations

▶There are six blank spaces in the story below. Four vocabulary words have already been used in the story. They are underlined. Use the other six words to fill the blank spaces.

In order to have singing as one's <u>métier</u>, one must first have the

_____ necessary to be successful. One must be

able to give good _____ of many types of songs.

A _____ use of talent, and an ability to <u>apply</u>

oneself to rigid schedules, help to bring fame. <u>Frantic</u> applause of the

audience can greet a _____ on the stage. Standing

_____ will be given to these artist at every concert.

Fans will always _____ for more music from

their favorite artists. And critics will <u>commend</u> notable performances.

12

━━━━━━━━━━━━━━━━ **FOR EXTRA CREDIT** ━━━━━━━━━━━━━━━━

Learn More About Famous Singers and Hawaii

▶ On a separate sheet of paper or in your notebook, do the three exercises below. Then turn them in to your teacher.

1 Name two other famous singers you admire. Name the biggest song hits they have sung. In a few sentences, tell what you like about their style of singing.

2 Imagine you are preparing an interview with Bette Midler for your school paper. Make a list of at least five questions you'd like to ask Bette about her career.

3 Hawaii is the 50th state. Write a short paragraph explaining several reasons why this state is different from all the other 49 states. You'll find the answers to this exercise in the *World Atlas* or in an encyclopedia.

14

⊁ 3 THE CHALLENGE

The challenge of climbing a mountain has attracted brave people. Many have failed. Some have been forced to give up. Others have fallen to their death or perished in severe blizzards.

Climbing Mount Everest has always been the mountaineer's dream. Towering 29,028 feet above sea level, the summit of Mount Everest stands higher than any other. Located in the Himalaya Mountains, this icy peak is one of the greatest challenges on earth.

Edmund Hillary was determined to scale this mountain. With his native guide, Tenzing, he called together a group of hardy mountaineers. Top physical condition was needed for this perilous journey.

Hillary led the way with his guide and climbing companion. For a while, the expedition went smoothly. He warned the other mountaineers about these hidden chasms.

Suddenly a snow ledge gave way, and Hillary fell. Tenzing slammed his pickaxe into the face of the ice-covered mountain, grabbed the life rope, dug in his heels, and held on. The falling man slowly came to a stop on the sheer face of the cliff—saved by a thin rope and a brave friend.

For a moment, Hillary had come close to death. But the hardy band of mountaineers continued their climb. Finally, they attained their goal. As the first to reach the summit of Mount Everest, they had made the mountaineer's dream come true.

⸻⸻⸻ UNDERSTANDING THE STORY ⸻⸻⸻

▶Circle the letter next to each correct statement.

1. When asked why he wanted to climb Mount Everest, a famous mountaineer replied, "Because it is there." He meant that
   a. there wasn't a mountain he couldn't climb.
   b. the challenge of conquering a mountain was reason enough.
   c. even if he failed, the mountain would still be there.

2. For a person to successfully climb a mountain such as Mount Everest, he or she must
   a. have great confidence in the bravery and skill of the other climbers on the expedition.
   b. spend millions of dollars on equipment and supplies.
   c. study in great detail the maps used by Edmund Hillary.

▶Here are the ten vocabulary words in this lesson. Write them in alphabetical order in the blank spaces below.

challenge	perished	hardy	expedition	chasms
summit	scale	attained	perilous	sheer

1. _____

2. _____

3. _____

4. _____

5. _____

6. _____

7. _____

8. _____

9. _____

10. _____

~~~~~~~~~~~~~ WHAT DO THE WORDS MEAN? ~~~~~~~~~~~~~

▶Here are some meanings for the ten vocabulary words in this lesson. Three words have been written beside their meanings. Write the other seven words next to their meanings.

1. _____ group of people undertaking a special journey, such as mountain climbing

2. _____ steep; straight up and down

3. _____ chasms _____ deep openings or cracks

4. _____ reached; achieved

5. _____ perished _____ died, usually in a violent manner

6. _____ peak; highest point

7. _____ a call to a contest or battle

8. _____ dangerous; hazardous

9. _____ hardy _____ able to take hard physical treatment; bold; daring

10. _____ climb

16

▰▰▰▰▰▰▰▰ COMPLETE THE SENTENCES ▰▰▰▰▰▰▰▰

▶ **Use the vocabulary words in this lesson to complete the following sentences. Use each word only once. The first one has been done for you.**

hardy	perilous	chasms	summit	sheer
scale	challenge	expedition	perished	attained

1. Before the _____expedition_____ could leave, years of planning were necessary.

2. Some people cannot resist the _____ of climbing a huge mountain.

3. Until they came to the _____ face of the cliff, the mountaineers had been making good progress.

4. If they had any chance to _____ the cliff, it would be because the two lead climbers were very experienced.

5. Only a very _____ person can stand the freezing temperatures.

6. They knew that the climb was _____, so they took safety precautions.

7. They had to watch out for hidden _____ into which climbers could fall.

8. Only three people reached the _____, although the others almost made it.

9. The group had _____ their goal, but at the terrible cost of two lives.

10. In memory of the climbers who had _____, they erected a stone marker.

▰▰▰▰▰▰▰▰▰ USE YOUR OWN WORDS ▰▰▰▰▰▰▰▰▰

▶ **Look at the picture. What words come into your mind other than the ten vocabulary words used in this lesson? Write them on the blank lines below. To help you get started, here are two good words:**

1. _____danger_____

2. _____snow_____

3. _____

4. _____

5. _____

6. _____

7. _____

8. _____

9. _____

10. _____

▶ Two of our vocabulary words, *summit* and *expedition*, are nouns. List as many words as you can which describe or tell something about the words *summit* and *expedition*. You can work on this with your classmates. Listed below are some words to help you get started.

summit	expedition
1. _____ high _____	1. _____ large _____
2. _____ cold _____	2. _____ careful _____
3. _____	3. _____
4. _____	4. _____
5. _____	5. _____
6. _____	6. _____
7. _____	7. _____
8. _____	8. _____

〰〰〰〰〰〰〰 **COMPLETE THE STORY** 〰〰〰〰〰〰〰

▶ Here are the ten vocabulary words for this lesson:

challenge	perished	hardy	expedition	chasms
summit	scale	attained	perilous	sheer

▶ There are six blank spaces in the story below. Four vocabulary words have already been used in the story. They are underlined. Use the other six words to fill in the blank spaces.

There are many high mountain peaks in the world that offer a great

_____ to mountaineers. For centuries, men and

women have tried to _____ their heights. The

_____ leader of an expedition must gather together

the best mountaineers and equipment. They must plan every step of

the way in order to achieve their goal. Despite their great skill and

bravery, many mountaineers have perished. Some have slipped on

the _____ face of a cliff and fallen into deep chasms.

Others have died in blizzards on their _____ journey.

When an expedition reaches the summit, there is great joy. The climb-

ers have _____ their goal of conquering a mountain.

Learn More About Mountain Climbing

▶On a separate sheet of paper or in your notebook, do the three exercises below. Then turn them in to your teacher.

1 Imagine yourself at the summit of Mount Everest. You are standing on the highest point on earth. Very few people have accomplished what you have done. Write a paragraph describing your feelings after you have reached the top.

2 There have been many famous and exciting books written about mountain climbing. Edmund Hillary wrote one about his conquest of Mount Everest. See if you can locate in your school or public library five titles of books that deal with mountain climbing. Name the mountains about which the books were written.

3 You are planning an expedition to climb the highest mountain in the United States. What is its name? In what state is this mountain located? How high is this mountain? Make a list of the equipment you will need for your climb.

❧ 4 AFRICAN-AMERICAN WRITER

The theater was hushed. The audience was ⬚intent⬚ on the action before them. For over two hours they sat alert, involved in the play. Suddenly, thunderous applause filled the air. Overnight, Ntozake Shange (en to ZAH kee SHANG gay) became the ⬚toast⬚ of Broadway. Her play, *For Colored Girls,* was an immediate hit.

Ntozake was born Paulette Williams. Her childhood was happy, free of the poverty and problems she writes about. Her family enjoyed ⬚cultural⬚ activities. She read many great Spanish, Russian, and French ⬚novels⬚ . "They were a big ⬚influence⬚ on me," she says. "My reading was more real to me than my real life."

Paulette majored in African-American poetry and music at Barnard College. It was then that she took the African name Ntozake Shange. Ntozake wrote about black women and their difficulties. The people she wrote about did not lead ⬚privileged⬚ lives. Her poems express their pain. Ntozake began reading her poems to school groups and poetry clubs. While she read, a friend ⬚extemporized⬚ music to fit her poems. Another improvised a dance to the rhythm of the words. That is how the play *For Colored Girls* got started.

⬚Recently⬚ she wrote a novel called *Betsy Brown.* It was so successful that it was made into a play for which Ntozake wrote the ⬚script⬚ . Success doesn't spoil Ntozake Shange. It ⬚spurs⬚ her on.

⬙⬙⬙⬙⬙⬙⬙⬙⬙⬙ UNDERSTANDING THE STORY ⬙⬙⬙⬙⬙⬙⬙⬙⬙⬙

▶**Circle the letter next to each correct statement.**

1. The main idea of this story is that
   a. Ntozake's father was the most important influence on her life.
   b. Ntozake's early interest in reading and African-American culture helped her to become a fine writer.
   c. changing her name from Paulette Williams to Ntozake Shange was a turning point in her life.

2. From this story, you can conclude that
   a. many more people will change their present names to African names.
   b. readers of Ntozake's works will have greater understanding of the feelings and experiences of black American women.
   c. Ntozake will turn her talent toward writing about the problems of men.

▶Here are the ten vocabulary words in this lesson. Write them in alphabetical order in the blank spaces below.

| toast | recently | spurs | influence | cultural |
| intent | privileged | novels | extemporized | script |

1._____ 6._____

2._____ 7._____

3._____ 8._____

4._____ 9._____

5._____ 10._____

~~~~~~~~~~ WHAT DO THE WORDS MEAN? ~~~~~~~~~~

▶Here are some meanings for the ten vocabulary words in this lesson. Three words have been written beside their meanings. Write the other seven words next to their meanings.

1._____ a short time ago; lately

2._____ urges on; encourages

3._____ written text of a play or movie

4._____ long stories about imaginary people and events

5._____ a popular and admired person

6._____privileged_____ having advantages

7._____cultural_____ relating to art, good taste, and education

8._____ performed without preparation

9._____ concentrating; paying close attention

10._____influence_____ motivating force

22

▶ Use the vocabulary words in this lesson to complete the following sentences. Use each word only once. The first one has been done for you.

toast	privileged	extemporized	script	novels
spurs	cultural	influence	recently	intent

1. Ntozake will tell you that her parents were a great ___influence___ on her life.

2. Their love of _____ activities opened up many areas of learning for her.

3. As a child she loved reading _____ because of the events described.

4. Ntozake is proud that her novel was _____ published.

5. She probably never dreamed she would be the _____ of Broadway.

6. She sympathizes with those who are not _____ but struggle to get by.

7. She is very _____ on expressing the feelings of many women today.

8. She and a few friends _____ music and dance to go with her poems.

9. She is now working on the _____ for the movie version of her new novel.

10. Knowing that more people will come to know her work _____ her on.

⚞⚟⚞⚟⚞⚟ USE YOUR OWN WORDS ⚞⚟⚞⚟⚞⚟

▶ Look at the picture. What words come into your mind other than the ten vocabulary words used in this lesson? Write them on the blank lines below. To help you get started, here are two good words:

1. _____creative_____
2. _____serious_____
3. _____
4. _____
5. _____
6. _____
7. _____
8. _____
9. _____
10. _____

ᴠᴠᴠᴠᴠᴠᴠᴠᴠᴠ FIND THE SUBJECTS AND PREDICATES ᴠᴠᴠᴠᴠᴠᴠᴠ

▶ The **subject** of a sentence names the person, place, or thing that is spoken about. The **predicate** of a sentence is what is said about the subject. For example:

> <u>The small boy</u> <u>went to the football game.</u>

▶ *The small boy* is the person the sentence is about, and *went to the football game* is the predicate of the sentence because it tells what the small boy did. **In the following sentences draw one line under the subject of the sentence and two lines under the predicate.**

1. Ntozake loved reading books.

2. African-American poetry and music were her majors in college.

3. A film company has offered to buy her new book.

4. Paulette Williams thought the name Ntozake Shange was better suited to her.

5. A person can express feelings very well through poetry.

ᴠᴠᴠᴠᴠᴠᴠᴠᴠᴠᴠᴠᴠ COMPLETE THE STORY ᴠᴠᴠᴠᴠᴠᴠᴠᴠᴠᴠ

▶ Here are the ten vocabulary words for this lesson:

toast	privileged	extemporized	script	novels
spurs	cultural	influence	recently	intent

▶ There are six blanks in the story below. Four vocabulary words have already been used in the story. They are underlined. Use the other six words to fill in the blank spaces.

Ntozake Shange grew up loving <u>cultural</u> things. The fine books, music,
and dance that she enjoyed had a big _____ on her.
They inspired her to be a poet and a playwright. They also helped her
to see the value of what she and her friends had done when they
_____ music and dance to fit her words.

　When Ntozake reads her poems, people become silent and listen
in an _____ way. She often writes about people who
have not had <u>privileged</u> lives. Her wish to see these people's stories
told _____ her on.

　<u>Recently</u>, a movie company bought the rights to her new book.
This book is probably only the first of many _____
she will write. She was asked to write the <u>script</u> for the movie version.
Soon she may be the _____ of Hollywood as well.

⟩⟩⟩⟩⟩⟩⟩⟩⟩⟩⟩⟩⟩⟩⟩⟩ FOR EXTRA CREDIT ⟨⟨⟨⟨⟨⟨⟨⟨⟨⟨⟨⟨⟨⟨

Learn More About Poetry, Novels, and Plays

▶**On a separate sheet of paper or in your notebook, do the three exercises below. Then turn them in to your teacher.**

1   The names of four important American poets are listed below. Select one and read some of the poems he or she has written. Choose your favorite from among these poems and read it to the class. Try to capture the feeling of the poem in your voice.

Langston Hughes	Gwendolyn Brooks
Emily Dickinson	Robert Frost

2   Ntozake Shange adapted one of her novels for the stage and made it into a play. If you could make a play out of your favorite book, how would you do it? Choose a short scene from the book and make it into a dramatic scene.

3   Go to the library with a few friends and select a one-act play. Practice reading the different parts aloud. Be ready to act out a small part of the play for the rest of the class. If your play can be presented better in song, mime, or dance, improvise a little.

JERUSALEM THE GOLDEN

Although this city has been invaded and destroyed, or partly destroyed, more than 40 times, it has always been rebuilt. Ruin has been piled upon ruin until today the streets are 35 feet higher than they were 2,000 years ago.

For ages Jerusalem has been a sacred city. It is the center of three religious groups—the Jews, the Christians, and the Muslims. For this reason Jerusalem has been called the land of the star, the cross, and the crescent . Each of these three symbols stands for one of the three religions. The star is the Star of David for the Jewish religion. The cross is the cross of Jesus for the Christian religion. The crescent is the symbol for the Muslim religion.

Jerusalem is divided into two parts—the old city and the new city. The new Jerusalem resembles a modern city. It has tall buildings and crowded streets. The old Jerusalem has hardly changed over its long history. Many of the towers and religious shrines that were built long ago still stand.

The clothes worn by the people of Jerusalem also reflect the old and the new. Some people wear the apparel of their forebears . Others dress in the latest styles.

New and old, Jews, Christians, and Muslims, all mingle in the narrow streets of Jerusalem. Both the beauty and importance of this great city have made it "Jerusalem the Golden."

UNDERSTANDING THE STORY

▶Circle the letter next to each correct statement.

1. The main idea of this story is that
   a. Jerusalem is a city torn by wars and in need of rebuilding.
   b. Jerusalem is a mix of the old and the new, and its people are a mix of different faiths.
   c. symbols are necessary to tell religions apart.

2. From this story, you can conclude that
   a. the days of the destruction of Jerusalem are over.
   b. millions of people have strong emotional ties to Jerusalem.
   c. people in the new part of the city are more religious than people in the old part.

▶Here are the ten vocabulary words in this lesson. Write them in alphabetical order in the blank spaces below.

sacred	crescent	shrines	apparel	forebears
religious	symbols	resembles	reflect	mingle

1. _____   6. _____

2. _____   7. _____

3. _____   8. _____

4. _____   9. _____

5. _____   10. _____

〰〰〰〰〰〰〰〰 WHAT DO THE WORDS MEAN? 〰〰〰〰〰〰〰〰

▶Here are some meanings for the ten vocabulary words in this lesson. Three words have been written beside their meanings. Write the other seven words next to their meanings.

1. _____ sacred _____ holy; worthy of reverence

2. _____ the shape of the moon in the first or last quarter; the symbol of the Muslim religion

3. _____ things that stand for or represent something else; signs

4. _____ having to do with a belief in God; devout

5. _____ resembles _____ looks like; similar in appearance

6. _____ sacred places; places where holy things are kept

7. _____ give back an image of

8. _____ apparel _____ clothing; dress

9. _____ family members who lived a long time ago

10. _____ mix; get along together

28

▶Use the vocabulary words in this lesson to complete the following sentences. Use each word only once. The first one has been done for you.

shrines	resembles	religious	sacred	reflect
apparel	symbols	crescent	mingle	forebears

1. Jerusalem is a city that has ____religious____ meaning for people of different faiths.

2. In buildings that were used by their _____ , the people worship daily.

3. Throughout Jerusalem one sees three famous _____ — the star, the cross, and the crescent.

4. The _____ is a symbol that has special meaning for the Muslim people.

5. The Western Wall is a structure that is _____ to the Jewish people.

6. The religious _____ in the old city are visited by people from far and near.

7. People of different races, religions, and styles _____ in the streets.

8. To judge by the _____ worn by the people in the old city, there has been little change over the centuries.

9. However, the new part of Jerusalem _____ most other modern cities.

10. The tall buildings in new Jerusalem _____ the modern tastes of people in that section of the city.

~~~~~~~~~~~~~~~~ USE YOUR OWN WORDS ~~~~~~~~~~~~~~~~

▶Look at the picture. What words come into your mind other than the ten vocabulary words used in this lesson? Write them on the blank lines below. To help you get started, here are two good words:

1. _____dome_____
2. _____window_____
3. _____
4. _____
5. _____
6. _____
7. _____
8. _____
9. _____
10. _____

▶ In an **analogy**, similar relationships occur between words that are different. For example, *pig* is to *hog* as *car* is to *automobile*. The relationship is that the words mean the same. Here's another analogy: *noisy* is to *quiet* as *short* is to *tall*. In this relationship, the words have opposite meanings. **See if you can complete the following analogies. Circle the correct word or words.**

1. **Crescent** is to **Muslim** as **star** is to
   a. sky   **b.** Christian   **c.** astronaut   **d.** Jewish

2. **Holy** is to **sacred** as **devout** is to
   a. man   **b.** child   **c.** religious   **d.** shrines

3. **Knowledge** is to **ignorance** as **mingle** is to
   a. mix   **b.** together   **c.** separate   **d.** truth

4. **Apparel** is to **body** as **shoe** is to
   a. shine   **b.** laces   **c.** leather   **d.** foot

5. **Sacred** is to **unholy** as **up** is to
   a. planes   **b.** down   **c.** sad   **d.** planets

COMPLETE THE STORY

▶ **Here are the ten vocabulary words for this lesson:**

sacred	crescent	shrines	apparel	forebears
religious	symbols	resembles	reflect	mingle

▶ **There are the six blank spaces in the story below. Four vocabulary words have already been used in the story. They are underlined. Use the other six words to fill in the blank spaces.**

Within old Jerusalem are three famous _____ that have been <u>sacred</u> to Christians, Jews, and Muslims for many centuries. While new Jerusalem _____ a modern city, the old city of the star, the cross, and the <u>crescent</u> has changed very little. These <u>symbols</u> _____ the many influences upon this city.

    Its narrow, winding streets are filled with people wearing the same kind of _____ that their <u>forebears</u> wore. Many very _____ people of different traditions meet and _____ with one another. If you visit this city, you can't help being touched by its history and culture.

Learn More About Shrines and Cities

▶On a separate sheet of paper or in your notebook, do the three exercises below. Then turn them in to your teacher.

1 There are three famous shrines in Jerusalem. They are: a) the Western Wall, also known as the Wailing Wall; b) the Church of the Holy Sepulcher; and c) the Dome of the Rock. Why are these places sacred to members of the three great religions? See what information, including pictures, you can bring to class about these shrines.

2 There are many famous cities in the world. Some of these are Rome, Paris, London, New York, Athens, and San Francisco. Take any famous city, and write a paragraph about it. If you want to write a description of your own hometown, that would be all right, too.

3 A good title must give some idea of what the story is about, and it must interest the reader. Write three other titles that might be used in place of "Jerusalem the Golden."

Corazon Aquino grew up on her parent's sugar-cane plantation on Luzon Island in the Philippines. Although her family expected her to lead a respectable but obscure life, she is now the much-loved President of the Philippines. Her story is perhaps as much a surprise to her as to her many admirers throughout the world.

Corazon was married to Benigno Aquino, the leader in the Philippine government of the opposition to former President Ferdinand Marcos. A much-feared dictator, Marcos forced his rival Aquino into exile in the United States. When Benigno returned to his homeland in 1983, he was immediately killed. The country was in turmoil. Over a million Filipinos signed a petition urging Aquino's widow to run for president. During her campaign, Corazon worked 16 hours a day. She acquired a lifetime of political experience and knowledge overnight. She began to articulate her policies with such confidence that she gained the respect of her followers. They saw in Corazon a greater opportunity to achieve freedom within their country. She was elected President of the Philippines.

Unifying a troubled country has not been an easy job. There have been great challenges and problems. Corazon has faced all hindrances with courage and dignity. She has changed the course both of her country's life and her own.

⬛⬛⬛⬛ UNDERSTANDING THE STORY ⬛⬛⬛⬛

▶ Circle the letter next to each correct statement.

1. The main idea of the story is that
   a. Corazon Aquino leads a respectable life.
   b. Corazon met the challenge of becoming president.
   c. the Filipinos have gained new freedoms.

2. From the story, you can conclude that
   a. Corazon has succeeded in her role as president.
   b. Marcos fled the country under pressure from the people.
   c. Corazon will be re-elected president.

▶Here are ten vocabulary words in the lesson. Write them in alphabetical order in the blank spaces below.

plantation	opposition	obscure	admirers	homeland
turmoil	petition	articulate	experience	hindrances

1. _____   6. _____

2. _____   7. _____

3. _____   8. _____

4. _____   9. _____

5. _____   10. _____

〰〰〰〰〰〰〰 WHAT DO THE WORDS MEAN? 〰〰〰〰〰〰〰

▶Here are some meanings for the ten vocabulary words in this lesson. Three words have been written beside their meaning. Write the other seven words next to their meanings.

1. _____ to express in clear verbal form

2. _____ those who respect or have high opinions of someone

3. _____hindrances_____ things that block a goal

4. _____ active participation in events

5. _____ place of origin

6. _____obscure_____ unnoticed; undistinguished

7. _____ a written document of request

8. _____ group against the government in power

9. _____ large estate or farm

10. _____turmoil_____ confusion; commotion

34

▶ Use the vocabulary words in this lesson to complete the following sentences. Use each word once. The first one has been done for you.

plantation	opposition	obscure	admirers	homeland
turmoil	petition	articulate	experience	hindrances

1. There was a very active ___opposition___ group against Ferdinand Marcos.

2. Corazon was raised on a large _____ which grew sugar cane.

3. It is important for a politician to be able to _____ his or her point of view.

4. Corazon feels much loyalty to her _____, the place of her birth.

5. The _____ that urged Corazon to run for president showed her support among the people.

6. Corazon's political intelligence has won her many _____ .

7. Corazon could have had an _____ , uneventful life.

8. When a major political leader is assassinated, there is usually much _____ among the people of the country.

9. As a politician, Corazon made up in energy and intelligence what she lacked in _____ .

10. Poverty in the Philippines is one of the _____ to its gaining success as a country of major influence.

~~~~~~~~~~~~~~~ USE YOUR OWN WORDS ~~~~~~~~~~~~~~~

▶ Look at the picture. What words come into your mind other than the ten vocabulary words used in the lesson? Write them on the blank lines below. To help you get started, here are two good words:

1. ___glasses___

2. ___pride___

3. _____

4. _____

5. _____

6. _____

7. _____

8. _____

9. _____

10. _____

35

▶The **possessive** of a word shows that something belongs to it. For example, Bill has a boat; it is *Bill's* boat. To make a possessive of a word that doesn't end in "s," add an apostrophe and an "s" to the word, such as *baker's* bread or *father's* car. To make a possessive of a word that does end in "s," add apostrophe (s') such as *friends'* bicycles or *ladies'* hats. (Exceptions: *Gus's* house; *Dickens's* books.) **Here are ten words from the story. In the blank space next to each word write the correct possessive of the word.**

1. admirers _____

2. dictator _____

3. petition _____

4. job _____

5. president _____

6. leader _____

7. Filipinos _____

8. life _____

9. plantation _____

10. days _____

▶**Here are the ten vocabulary words for this lesson:**

plantation	opposition	obscure	admirer	homeland
turmoil	petition	articulate	experience	hindrances

▶**There are six blanks in the story below. Four vocabulary words have already been used in the story. They are underlined. Use the other six words to fill in the blank spaces.**

Like many people, Corazon Aquino was raised with the expectation she would lead an _____, quiet life. Her girlhood on her parent's <u>plantation</u>, or estate, was not exceptional. As she grew older she was devoted to her _____, but she had no direct _____ in politics. Although she was an _____ of her husband Benigno's politics, she was well aware of the many <u>hindrances</u> that faced him as he led the _____ movement to the Marcos government. When Benigno was assassinated, his followers were thrown into a state of _____. They knew, however, that they wanted Corazon to lead them. They drew up a _____ which many hopeful supporters signed. Perhaps the first words Corazon had to publicly <u>articulate</u> was her pledge to work for the freedom and well-being of her fellow Filipinos.

Learn More About the Philippines and Women in Politics

▶On a separate sheet of paper or in your notebook, do the three exercises below. Then turn them in to your teacher.

1   Margaret Thatcher of Great Britain and Benazir Bhutto of Pakistan were two powerful leaders. As Prime Ministers, they decided on the policies their countries followed. Research the life and political career of either Margaret Thatcher or Benazir Bhutto. Prepare a brief talk for your classmates.

2   In the U.S. today, many women are in leadership positions. Four such women are listed below. In a few sentences for each, describe her job and two or three interesting facts about her life.

Ann Richards   Sharon Pratt Dixon
Patricia Schroeder   Sandra Day O'Connor

3   Before Corazon Aquino was elected president of the Philippines, Ferdinand Marcos ruled the country. The government under Marcos was very different. Research the political ideas of both Marcos and Corazon Aquino. Make a comparison. Present your ideas in a panel discussion.

RANDY TRAVIS: A NEW KIND OF COUNTRY BOY

7

Country songs often tell of somebody's troubles. When Randy Travis sings, the words have real meaning for him. He was born near Marshville, North Carolina. His family worked hard, but his father **urged** his boys to take up the guitar. Travis practiced and gave his first performance at the age of eight.

Later on, those troubles started for Travis. He dropped out of school in the ninth grade. He argued with his parents and was in constant trouble. He was even **arrested** five times for drug and drink-related incidents. Today, he shrugs and says, "Now, I wouldn't have the **ignorance** or nerve to do those things."

His life was **altered** when he met Lib Hatcher. She owned a restaurant, and she hired Randy to cook, clean up, and sing for the customers. During this period, she helped him straighten out his life. One night, a **talent** scout from Warner Records heard Travis sing. She immediately gave him a **contract** . His first record was released twice. The first time it didn't even make the top fifty. The second time it **soared** to number one on the charts.

Today, Travis travels much of the year. Hatcher is his business **manager** and his best friend. Travis no longer needs the money. He just likes to perform for his fans. "They feel like family when they like you," he admits, with a **shy** smile. Travis still has one goal. He has received 43 awards for his singing, but he wants to be **recognized** as a songwriter, too. Today most of his troubles seem to be the ones expressed in his songs.

UNDERSTANDING THE STORY

▶ Circle the letter next to each correct statement.

1. The main idea of this story is that
   a. Randy Travis was a wild teenager.
   b. country music is popular.
   c. country music changed Travis's life.

2. Randy Travis knows what country songs are about because
   a. his own life has been easy and unhurried.
   b. his early life was full of trouble and pain.
   c. he was born in North Carolina.

39

WWWWWWWWWW **MAKE AN ALPHABETICAL LIST** WWWWWWWWWW

▶ Here are the ten vocabulary words in this lesson. Write them in alphabetical order in the blank spaces below.

urged	arrested	ignorance	altered	talent
contract	manager	recognized	soared	shy

1. _____   6. _____

2. _____   7. _____

3. _____   8. _____

4. _____   9. _____

5. _____   10. _____

WWWWWWWWWW **WHAT DO THE WORDS MEAN?** WWWWWWWWWW

▶ Here are some meanings for the ten vocabulary words in this lesson. Three words have been written beside their meanings. Write the other seven words next to their meanings.

1. _____ lack of knowledge

2. ____contract____ a legal paper promising a job

3. _____ a natural gift for doing something

4. _____ identified

5. ____manager____ a performer's business arranger

6. _____ held by the police

7. ____urged____ advised strongly

8. _____ changed

9. _____ modest; uncertain

10. _____ rose upward quickly

40

ᴡᴡᴡᴡᴡᴡᴡᴡᴡ COMPLETE THE SENTENCES ᴡᴡᴡᴡᴡᴡᴡᴡᴡ

▶Use the vocabulary words in this lesson to complete the following sentences. Use each word only once. The first one has been done for you.

urged	arrested	ignorance	altered	talent
contract	manager	recognized	soared	shy

1. Time has _____altered_____ Randy Travis's feelings about life.

2. He thinks his _____ got him into trouble.

3. He was _____ , but he never went to prison.

4. He has a natural _____ for singing country songs.

5. His _____ and best friend put him to work in a restaurant that she owned.

6. An executive from a large record company heard Travis sing and offered him a _____ .

7. Travis is _____ when he talks about his success as a singer.

8. He would really like to be _____ as a songwriter.

9. He is still glad that his father _____ him to practice his singing and guitar playing.

10. His popularity has _____ , and he is one of America's best-known singers.

ᴡᴡᴡᴡᴡᴡᴡᴡᴡᴡᴡᴡ USE YOUR OWN WORDS ᴡᴡᴡᴡᴡᴡᴡᴡᴡᴡᴡ

▶Look at the picture. What words come into your mind other than the ten vocabulary words used in this lesson? Write them on the blank lines below. To help you get started, here are two good words:

1. _____cheerful_____
2. _____performer_____
3. _____
4. _____
5. _____
6. _____
7. _____
8. _____
9. _____
10. _____

▶**Antonyms** are words that are opposite in meaning. For example, *good* and *bad, fast* and *slow* are antonyms. **Here are antonyms for six of the vocabulary words. See if you can find the vocabulary words, and write them in the blank spaces on the left.**

Vocabulary Word	Antonym
1. _____	unchanged
2. _____	boastful
3. _____	wisdom
4. _____	dropped
5. _____	unknown
6. _____	discouraged

┅┅┅ COMPLETE THE STORY ┅┅┅

▶**Here are the ten vocabulary words for this lesson:**

urged	arrested	ignorance	altered	talent
contract	manager	recognized	soared	shy

▶**There are six blank spaces in the story below. Four vocabulary words have already been used in the story. They are underlined. Use the other six words to fill in the blank spaces.**

Randy Travis is _____ in interviews. He seems surprised that people recognize him. He talks about being _____ and other teenage troubles. He doesn't know why he broke the law. He claims his <u>ignorance</u> got him into trouble. Lib Hatcher _____ his life. She gave him his first job. She _____ him to sing for her customers. She <u>recognized</u> his _____ as a country singer. That job led to a recording <u>contract</u>. Hatcher is his business _____ now. His popularity <u>soared</u>, but he still thinks of himself as a country boy.

FOR EXTRA CREDIT

Learn More About Country Music

▶On a separate sheet of paper or in your notebook, do the three exercises below. Then turn them in to your teacher.

1 Country music has had many stars. Do research to find out about one of these performers: Tex Ritter, Patsy Cline, Hank Williams, Minnie Pearl, Loretta Lynn. Write a paragraph telling about the person you have chosen. Try to include the titles of songs the person has made famous.

2 Imagine that you are a country music star. You are about to come onstage. You can hear your fans cheering. What feelings would you have? Would you be nervous or excited? Write a short paragraph describing how a country singer might feel just before a performance.

3 Randy Travis and other country singers like to sing at the Grand Ole Opry in Nashville, Tennessee. In your school or public library, do research on the Opry. Find out when it started and the names of some of its famous stars. You might also find information about the recent development of Opryland U.S.A.

44

THE END OF THE BLUE WHALE?

Whales are among the largest, most powerful animals that have ever lived. Some dinosaurs were small by comparison. The blue whale, the largest of all whales, can grow to over 100 feet and weigh 150 tons. Despite its ⬚tremendous⬚ size, the blue whale is ⬚vulnerable⬚ to people's hunting ability.

The blue whale was first hunted by the North American Inuit (Eskimos). In fact, the whale was ⬚essential⬚ to the Inuit's existence. For centuries they hunted these huge ⬚mammals⬚ . They used the whales for food, but nothing was wasted. The whale oil became fuel. The sinews became ropes. The bones were used as tools.

Today the blue whale is still hunted by some nations. Its oil is used to make soap and other products. But there are alternative sources for all of these products. People no longer need to hunt blue whales to survive.

Modern-day whalers use advanced ⬚apparatus⬚ . Radar and helicopters are used to find the whales. Deadly ⬚harpoon⬚ guns are used to kill them. The ⬚carnage⬚ resulting from the use of this equipment has brought the blue whale close to extinction.

⬚Conservationists⬚ have warned us. If we allow whalers to continue in this way, ⬚extermination⬚ of the blue whale is almost certain.

It would be a shameful loss if the number of blue whales ⬚dwindled⬚ to nothing. The blue whale can never be replaced.

〰〰〰〰〰〰〰 **UNDERSTANDING THE STORY** 〰〰〰〰〰〰〰

▶ **Circle the letter next to each correct statement.**

1. The main purpose of this story is to
   a. describe the features of the blue whale.
   b. warn readers that a great animal is in danger of becoming extinct.
   c. describe the many ways the Inuit used whales in their daily life.

2. From this story, you can conclude that
   a. it is only a rumor that the blue whale is in danger of becoming extinct.
   b. the blue whale has learned to avoid the deadly harpoon gun.
   c. the public must do something soon if the blue whale is to survive.

►Here are the ten vocabulary words in this lesson. Write them in alphabetical order in the blank spaces below.

tremendous	mammals	harpoon	conservationists	dwindled
extermination	essential	apparatus	carnage	vulnerable

1. _____   6. _____

2. _____   7. _____

3. _____   8. _____

4. _____   9. _____

5. _____   10. _____

~~~~~~~~~~~~~ WHAT DO THE WORDS MEAN? ~~~~~~~~~~~~~

►Here are some meanings for the ten vocabulary words in this lesson. Three words have been written beside their meanings. Write the other seven words next to their meanings.

1. _____ huge; enormous

2. _____carnage_____ killing of a great number of people or animals

3. _____ animals that feed milk to their young; people belong to this group

4. _____ very important

5. _____apparatus_____ materials, tools, special instruments, or machinery needed to carry out a purpose

6. _____ persons who wish to save forms of animal and plant life in danger of being destroyed forever

7. _____ a long spear with a rope tied to it used in killing a whale

8. _____vulnerable_____ defenseless against; open to attack or injury

9. _____ the act of destroying completely, putting an end to

10. _____ reduced in number

46

∎∎∎∎∎∎∎ COMPLETE THE SENTENCES ∎∎∎∎∎∎∎

▶Use the vocabulary words in this lesson to complete the following sentences. Use each word only once. The first one has been done for you.

apparatus	harpoon	extermination	tremendous	vulnerable
dwindled	mammals	essential	carnage	conservationists

1. Not enough is being done to prevent the __**extermination**__ of the blue whale.

2. Whales have become more _____ to extermination because of improvements in hunting equipment.

3. In some areas, the number of blue whales has _____ to only a few dozen.

4. Animals that feed milk to their young are called _____ .

5. The _____ used to hunt whales today is very advanced.

6. Because the whale was _____ to the Inuit's existence, it had to be hunted.

7. The _____ of the whale that still goes on today is harder to excuse.

8. The _____ that used to be thrown by a person is now shot out of a gun.

9. _____ are calling on people to outlaw the unnecessary killing of whales.

10. It's hard to imagine the _____ size of a blue whale until you have seen one.

∎∎∎∎∎∎∎∎∎ USE YOUR OWN WORDS ∎∎∎∎∎∎∎∎∎

▶Look at the picture. What words come into your mind other than the ten vocabulary words used in this lesson? Write them on the blank lines below. To help you get started, here are two good words:

1. _____water_____
2. _____splash_____
3. _____
4. _____
5. _____
6. _____
7. _____
8. _____
9. _____
10. _____

▶The **possessive** of a word shows that something belongs to it. For example, Bill has a boat; it is *Bill's* boat. To make a possessive of a word that doesn't end in "s," add an apostrophe and an "s" to the word, such as *baker's* bread or *father's* car. To make a possessive of a word that does end in "s," add an apostrophe (s'), such as *friends'* bicycles or *ladies'* hats.

▶**Here are ten words from the story. In the blank space next to the word write the correct possessive of the word.**

1. ships _____
2. fleet _____
3. ocean _____
4. bodies _____
5. whale _____

6. Inuit _____
7. blubber _____
8. cosmetics _____
9. number _____
10. whaleboats _____

━━━━━━━━━ **COMPLETE THE STORY** ━━━━━━━━━

▶**Here are the ten vocabulary words for this lesson:**

extermination	tremendous	harpoon	apparatus	dwindled
conservationists	essential	carnage	vulnerable	mammals

▶**There are six blank spaces in the story below. Four vocabulary words have already been used in the story. They are underlined. Use the other six words to fill in the blank spaces.**

The blue whale is the largest animal that has ever lived. However,

_____ are worried. If whalers keep killing these

huge _____ , the blue whale is doomed to

extermination.

Sixty years ago there were many blue whales in the world. Today

the number has _____ to very few. The deadly

_____ gun is the major reason for this. But whalers

have other modern apparatus to help them find and kill the whales.

The common use of helicopters and radar makes the whales very

_____ .

It is essential that the killing of this _____ animal

be stopped. If the carnage continues, the blue whale will completely

disappear from the oceans of the world.

~~~~~~~~~~~~ FOR EXTRA CREDIT ~~~~~~~~~~~~~~

Learn More About Whales

▶On a separate sheet of paper or in your notebook, do the three exercises below. Then turn them in to your teacher.

1 The title of this selection is "The End of the Blue Whale?" Can you think of other titles that may work even better? Give it a try. On a sheet of paper, make up at least three titles that could be used for this story.

2 Imagine you are writing a letter to the Secretary General of the United Nations asking him to stop the killing of blue whales. What suggestions would you make to him? Think about it for a while. You might even discuss your ideas with your friends and parents. When you have decided what you want to say, write a letter.

3 Besides the blue whale, there are many other animals that are in danger of complete extermination. Look up "Endangered Wildlife" in the *World Almanac*. Choose three examples from the list of endangered mammals. Then write a short paragraph about the animals you have chosen. Include the names of the mammals, where they live, and how many are believed left in the world.

9 THE RETURN OF THE *MARY ROSE*

In 1545, the pride of the British navy, the *Mary Rose*, set sail. Its mission was to fight the French. Among those watching from shore was the monarch , Henry VIII. The crowd was cheering when the ship left Portsmouth harbor. The outcome, however, was disaster. The 700-ton *Mary Rose* was laden with cannons. Before it got far from shore, it sank. Historians say the cannons were not properly bolted . The loose cannons rolled across the deck and through the ship's side. In rushed the sea. Over 650 sailors lost their lives. It was a grave blow to the British people and their king.

Over 420 years later, the *Mary Rose* was found. A diver, Alexander McKee, discovered the wreck a mile off the coast of England. For four years, McKee and his friends worked to clear away mud and silt. They finally brought up a cannon. This find stirred the public's interest. Money was contributed to raise the *Mary Rose*. Prince Charles became president of the Mary Rose Trust, which raised funds.

The salvage continued during the summer of 1982. With the use of a special lifting crane and cradle , the *Mary Rose* was brought to the surface. Most of its oak frame was still in fair condition. To prevent further decay, the hull was wrapped in plastic sheeting. Sea water was constantly sprayed on the timbers to preserve them. The rescue marked the end of a 17-year-long project . The cost had been seven million dollars. But it was worth every penny. The restored *Mary Rose* is now on permanent display in England.

~~~~~~~~~ UNDERSTANDING THE STORY ~~~~~~~~~

▶Circle the letter next to each correct statement.

1. The main idea of this story is that
   a. it took seven million dollars to raise the *Mary Rose*.
   b. the *Mary Rose* sank without firing a shot at the enemy.
   c. after more than 400 years at the bottom of the sea, the *Mary Rose* was salvaged.

2. From this story, you can conclude that
   a. Prince Charles will continue to search for lost wrecks.
   b. from now on cannons aboard ships will be more securely bolted.
   c. British pride was given a great lift by the rescue of the *Mary Rose*.

MAKE AN ALPHABETICAL LIST

▶Here are the ten vocabulary words in this lesson. Write them in alphabetical order in the blank spaces below.

plastic	mission	laden	restored	project
monarch	bolted	cradle	salvage	grave

1. _____   6. _____

2. _____   7. _____

3. _____   8. _____

4. _____   9. _____

5. _____   10. _____

WHAT DO THE WORDS MEAN?

▶Here are some meanings for the ten vocabulary words in this lesson. Three words have been written beside their meanings. Write the other seven words next to their meanings.

1. _____ an undertaking, often a big, complicated job

2. _____ king or queen; an absolute ruler

3. _____cradle_____ a framework upon which a ship rests, usually during repair

4. _____ fastened; held with metal fittings

5. _____mission_____ a special task

6. _____ a synthetic or processed material

7. _____grave_____ serious; critical

8. _____ the act of saving a ship or its cargo from the sea

9. _____ loaded; heavily burdened

10. _____ brought back to its original state; reconstructed

52

▶Use the vocabulary words in this lesson to complete the following sentences. Use each word only once. The first one has been done for you.

bolted	plastic	monarch	laden	restored
cradle	grave	project	salvage	mission

1. We knew that the ____salvage____ was successful when we saw the ship's mast.

2. The cargo was securely _____ to the deck so that it wouldn't roll.

3. It may take three years for the ship to be _____ to its former glory.

4. The king said, "Your _____ is to seek out and destroy the enemy."

5. Little did the _____ know that his favorite ship would soon sink.

6. The problem was that the ship was _____ with heavy cannons.

7. The _____ involved hundreds of people and millions of dollars.

8. A steel _____ was designed to support the waterlogged ship.

9. The loss of 650 sailors was a _____ blow to the British people.

10. _____ was wrapped around the decaying hull to keep it from the air.

▶Look at the picture. What words come into your mind other than the ten vocabulary words used in this lesson? Write them on the blank lines below. To help you get started, here are two good words:

1. ____mechanical____
2. ____calm____
3. _____
4. _____
5. _____
6. _____
7. _____
8. _____
9. _____
10. _____

▶ Here are some words selected from the world of sailing and ships. See if you can match the terms with their meanings. You may need the help of a dictionary.

1. _____ hull   **a.** left-hand side of ship

2. _____ port   **b.** long pole holding sails

3. _____ starboard   **c.** vertical blade at rear of ship, used to change course

4. _____ stern   **d.** body of ship

5. _____ mast   **e.** having to do with ships and sailors

6. _____ rudder   **f.** back or rear of ship

7. _____ nautical   **g.** right-hand side of ship

~~~~~~~~~ COMPLETE THE STORY ~~~~~~~~~

▶ Here are the ten vocabulary words for this lesson:

monarch	restored	project	laden	cradle
salvage	bolted	grave	plastic	mission

▶ There are six blank spaces in the story below. Four vocabulary words have already been used in the story. They are underlined. Use the other six words to fill in the blank spaces.

The _____ Henry VIII was in a good mood. His fleet was on its way to fight the French. It was a <u>mission</u> that he strongly supported. He was particularly proud of the flagship, the *Mary Rose*. It was _____ with 91 cannons. What firepower!

Then suddenly everything went wrong. The heavy cannons were not _____ well enough. They rolled across the deck and crashed through the ship's side. The ship went down. Many sailors were drowned. What a <u>grave</u> loss to the nation. But 437 years later, the *Mary Rose* was <u>restored</u> to life. A _____ operation brought it to the surface. It was a huge <u>project</u> but it succeeded. A special steel _____ was built to raise the hull. As soon as the hull reappeared, it was wrapped in _____ to prevent further decay. The *Mary Rose* was home again.

~~~~~~~~~~~~~~~~~~~~~~~~~ FOR EXTRA CREDIT ~~~~~~~~~~~~~~~~~~~~~~~~~

Learn More About the *Mary Rose* and Other Lost Treasures

▶ On a separate sheet of paper or in your notebook, do the three exercises below. Then turn them in to your teacher.

1 The story of the *Mary Rose* is a fascinating one. When the ship finally returned to the surface on October 11, 1982, it was a major news story. *Time* and *Newsweek* magazines both contained articles about it. See how much more information you can find about this salvage operation. Ask your librarian for help.

2 Among the objects removed from the *Mary Rose* were articles of clothing, kitchen utensils, and bows and arrows. Make a list of other items you think were found aboard the ship. Imagine the preparations that must have been made to get hundreds of men ready for a naval battle.

3 It is said that a fortune in gold, jewelry, and ancient coins lies beneath the sea. Some of these treasures have already been found in the Caribbean and off the coast of Florida. Bring to class any pictures or stories you find about the search for undersea treasure. Make a bulletin board display of pictures and articles dealing with this topic.

It is the first night of your camping trip. You are sitting with your friends around the campfire. You think back to the day's activities. You were fascinated by all the spectacular sights.

Your guide interrupts your thoughts and begins to tell a chilling story. "A gigantic, wild, hairy beast that looks and walks like a man roams all over this country," the guide says. "Many reputable people claim to have seen it. One rancher says he has taken motion pictures of it. No one knows where this creature comes from or where he goes. And no one has been able to identify him. He is called Bigfoot."

You are skeptical about the whole story. "It makes good fiction," you think to yourself, "but it couldn't be true." Later, as you begin to fall asleep, you decide the story is nothing but a hoax.

Soon you are jolted awake by the shouts of one of your companions—"There he is!" You quickly look in the direction he is pointing. A huge animal, covered with dark hair, is coming toward you. But the shouts scare the primitive beast away.

The next morning you think there must be an explanation for what happened. Was it a dream? But soon you find proof: trampled grass and a few broken branches. No, it wasn't a dream. As you get ready for breakfast, you wonder, "Have I seen Bigfoot?"

UNDERSTANDING THE STORY

▶ Circle the letter next to each correct statement.

1. The main purpose of this story is to
   a. cause the reader to wonder if Bigfoot really exists.
   b. show how exciting camping can be with the right people along.
   c. convince the reader that there really is a Bigfoot.

2. From this story, you can conclude that
   a. the story of Bigfoot has finally been proven untrue.
   b. there will probably always be reports of seeing Bigfoot.
   c. Bigfoot is really an especially huge bear.

⚍⚍⚍⚍⚍⚍⚍⚍⚍⚍ MAKE AN ALPHABETICAL LIST ⚍⚍⚍⚍⚍⚍⚍⚍

▶Here are the ten vocabulary words in this lesson. Write them in alphabetical order in the blank spaces below.

fascinated	reputable	skeptical	hoax	explanation
spectacular	identify	fiction	primitive	proof

1. _____   6. _____

2. _____   7. _____

3. _____   8. _____

4. _____   9. _____

5. _____   10. _____

⚍⚍⚍⚍⚍⚍⚍⚍⚍⚍ WHAT DO THE WORDS MEAN? ⚍⚍⚍⚍⚍⚍⚍⚍

▶Here are some meanings for the ten vocabulary words in this lesson. Three words have been written beside their meanings. Write the other seven words next to their meanings.

1. _____skeptical_____ having doubts; not willing to believe

2. _____ a trick

3. _____ recognize as being a particular person or thing

4. _____ amazed; very interested by

5. _____fiction_____ a story that is not true

6. _____ facts; evidence

7. _____ honorable; well thought of

8. _____ eye-catching; very unusual

9. _____primitive_____ living long ago; from earliest times

10. _____ a statement that clears up a difficulty or mistake

▰▰▰▰▰▰▰▰▰▰ COMPLETE THE SENTENCES ▰▰▰▰▰▰▰▰▰▰

► Use the vocabulary words in this lesson to complete the following sentences. Use each word only once. The first one has been done for you.

fiction	skeptical	proof	explanation	fascinated
spectacular	hoax	primitive	identify	reputable

1. People have always been _____fascinated_____ by stories of strange creatures.

2. The story of Bigfoot seems closer to science _____ than to fact.

3. A professor called the story a _____ , even though she had seen the photographs of the so-called monster.

4. She said that she needed more _____ , such as a clear photograph.

5. Her _____ of the trampled grass and broken branches wasn't convincing.

6. She wasn't able to _____ a piece of hair found clinging to a branch.

7. Because those who claim to have seen Bigfoot are _____ , I tend to believe them.

8. The camper had seen so many _____ sights that day, his eyes were tired.

9. The police were _____ when two people in different places reported seeing Bigfoot at the same time.

10. The monster is called _____ because it seems like something prehistoric.

▰▰▰▰▰▰▰▰▰▰ USE YOUR OWN WORDS ▰▰▰▰▰▰▰▰▰▰

► Look at the picture. What words come into your mind other than the ten vocabulary words used in this lesson? Write them on the blank lines below. To help you get started, here are two good words:

1. _____leaves_____
2. _____hairy_____
3. _____
4. _____
5. _____
6. _____
7. _____
8. _____
9. _____
10. _____

59

▶Look at the vocabulary word *reputable*. See how many words you can form by using the letters of this word. Make up at least ten words. One has already been done for you. Write your words in the spaces below.

reputable

1. _____plate_____   7. _____

2. _____   8. _____

3. _____   9. _____

4. _____   10. _____

5. _____   11. _____

6. _____   12. _____

■■■■■■■■■■■■■■ COMPLETE THE STORY ■■■■■■■■■■■■■■

▶Here are the ten vocabulary words for this lesson:

fascinated	reputable	skeptical	hoax	explanation
spectacular	identify	fiction	primitive	proof

▶There are six blank spaces in the story below. Four vocabulary words have already been used in the story. They are underlined. Use the other six words to fill in the blank spaces.

Many_____ people claim they have seen Bigfoot, although scientists are_____ about this beast. Some experts think Bigfoot is nothing but a hoax.

One thing is for sure. Huge footprints have been found in the areas where the primitive creature roams. No one has been able to_____ these spectacular tracks. No one has ever seen anything like them before.

Bigfoot has_____ many people. Some believe Bigfoot is real, others say it is just_____. Scientists hope to gather more_____ about Bigfoot. Then, hopefully, we will have an explanation about this strange, mysterious creature.

60

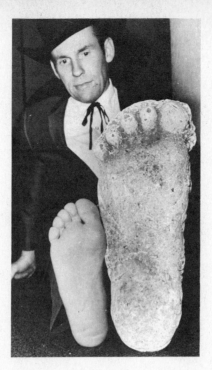

Learn More About Monsters

▶ **On a separate sheet of paper or in your notebook, do the three exercises below. Then turn them in to your teacher.**

1   Bigfoot is not the world's only mysterious creature. There are also the Loch Ness Monster and the Abominable Snowman. Go to the library and do some research on these two creatures. Then write several paragraphs about them. Be sure to include a description of both "monsters."

2   Prepare a reading list of books and articles about Bigfoot, the Abominable Snowman, and the Loch Ness Monster. Discuss them with your classmates. Ask your teacher or librarian for help on this exercise.

3   Who is your favorite monster? We have read about or seen many strange creatures on TV or in the movies. Three well-known examples are Frankenstein's monster, Count Dracula, and King Kong. Describe your favorite monster or unusual creature in a paragraph. How does it compare with Bigfoot?

✗ 11 THE LEARNING MAN ✗

Gordon Parks is a notable photographer. People love his pictures because he uses his camera the way a painter uses a brush.

Parks learned about photography at a Chicago art center. He became enthusiastic about the idea of pursuing a career in this field. To earn money, he worked as a waiter, a lumberjack, and a piano player. He led a band. He even played baseball.

Everyone saw that Gordon Parks's talent was considerable . He won a scholarship . Now he had an opportunity to study without worrying about money.

In time, Gordon Parks became a top magazine photographer. He traveled all over the world creating wonderful stories in pictures. Among his assignments were stories on segregation and crime and a report on the life of a gang leader in Harlem. He made a film documentary of his story on the plight of a poor boy in Brazil.

The accomplishments of this man are many. Parks is known for his original music. He is a master of the film documentary. His novel, *The Learning Tree,* is based on his life. It was made into a movie, which Parks produced, directed, and photographed. In 1989, *The Learning Tree* was declared one of the national treasures of American film.

Gordon Parks has found time for not one profession but three— photography, music, and writing—and has reached the top in all three.

~~~~~~~~~~~~~ UNDERSTANDING THE STORY ~~~~~~~~~~~~~

▶ Circle the letter next to each correct statement.

1. The main idea of this story is that
   a. Gordon won a scholarship that allowed him to study photography.
   b. Gordon is a master of the film documentary.
   c. Gordon is a person of many accomplishments.

2. From this story, you can conclude that
   a. Gordon's wide experience is helpful to him in his work.
   b. Gordon will win an Academy Award for one of his film documentaries.
   c. Gordon is ruining his health by trying to do too much.

▶Here are the ten vocabulary words in this lesson. Write them in alphabetical order in the blank spaces below.

notable	enthusiastic	scholarship	documentary	assignments
pursuing	profession	considerable	segregation	plight

1. _____ 6. _____

2. _____ 7. _____

3. _____ 8. _____

4. _____ 9. _____

5. _____ 10. _____

~~~~~~~~~~~~~ WHAT DO THE WORDS MEAN? ~~~~~~~~~~~~~

▶Here are some meanings for the ten vocabulary words in this lesson. Three words have been written beside their meanings. Write the other seven words next to their meanings.

1. _____profession_____ an occupation requiring an education

2. _____ striving for

3. _____ money given to help a student pay for studies

4. _____ definite tasks or jobs to be done; specific works to be accomplished

5. _____enthusiastic_____ eagerly interested

6. _____ factual presentation of a scene, place, or condition of life in writing or on film

7. _____ condition or state, usually bad

8. _____ worthy of notice; remarkable

9. _____considerable_____ not a little; much

10. _____ separation from others; setting individuals or groups apart from society

64

COMPLETE THE SENTENCES

▶ Use the vocabulary words in this lesson to complete the following sentences. Use each word only once. The first one has been done for you.

scholarship	considerable	assignments	plight	notable
pursuing	profession	enthusiastic	segregation	documentary

1. The film _____documentary_____ , *The Learning Tree*, is based on Gordon Parks's life.

2. To succeed in one _____ is good, but to succeed in three is exceptional.

3. You are happy to accept all sorts of _____ if you are a young photographer just breaking into the field.

4. Among Parks's _____ achievements is a documentary about a boy in Brazil.

5. The _____ of the poor has always interested Gordon.

6. The critics were most _____ in their reviews of Gordon's latest film.

7. If he had not received a _____ , he could not have finished school.

8. As director, he spent _____ time interviewing actors before picking a lead.

9. Gordon made people more aware of the problem of _____ and in this way helped to bring about social change.

10. Gordon is a person who believes in _____ something if it interests him.

USE YOUR OWN WORDS

▶ Look at the picture. What words come into your mind other than the ones you just matched with their meanings? Write them on the blank lines below. To help you get started, here are two good words:

1. _____moustache_____
2. _____camera_____
3. _____
4. _____
5. _____
6. _____
7. _____
8. _____
9. _____
10. _____

65

▶The **subject** of a sentence names the person, place, or thing that is spoken about. The **predicate** of a sentence is what is said about the subject. For example:

> **The small boy**   went to the football game.

▶*The small boy* is the person the sentence is about, and *went to the football game* is the predicate of the sentence because it tells what the small boy did. **In the following sentences draw one line under the subject of the sentence and two lines under the predicate of the sentence.**

1. I hungered for learning.

2. A scholarship allowed me to finish my education.

3. Two assignments impressed me.

4. The other was a documentary which I wrote.

5. My most notable achievement was writing the book.

▶Here are the ten vocabulary words for this lesson:

considerable	assignments	enthusiastic	notable	pursuing
profession	scholarship	documentary	plight	segregation

▶There are six blank spaces in the story below. Four vocabulary words have already been used in the story. They are underlined. Use the other six words to fill in the blank spaces.

Gordon Parks has had underlined considerable success in not one

_____ but three. However, his most

_____ assignments have been on one subject—

people.

Parks's _____ love of humanity is shown in many

of the picture stories he has photographed over the years. One partic-

ular documentary about a Brazilian boy shows what it is like to be poor.

His novel, *The Learning Tree,* which is based on his own life shows

the _____ of people who must live under segregation.

It all started for Parks when he was awarded a

_____ many years ago. Since then, he has been

_____ one special goal—to show how people live.

Hopefully, his work will teach us to better understand each other.

▚▚▚▚▚▚▚▚▚▚▚▚▚▚▚▚▚▚▚▚ FOR EXTRA CREDIT ▚▚▚▚▚▚▚▚▚▚▚▚▚▚▚▚▚▚▚▚

Learn More About People

▶ **On a separate sheet of paper or in your notebook, do the three exercises below. Then turn them in to your teacher.**

1 Mathew Brady is one of the most famous American photographers. Find out about Brady in your school library. Then write a few paragraphs about him. Be sure to mention when Brady lived. Also include several of his accomplishments. Brady is famous for taking pictures of a particular war.

2 When *The Learning Tree* was made into a movie, there were many people who worked behind the scenes. Go to your library and find a book that describes the jobs people perform on a movie set. Then write a definition for each of the following movie jobs:

    1. director   3. screenwriter   5. costume designer
    2. producer   4. editor   6. gaffer

3 Produce your own documentary. Read newspaper or magazine articles on any topic that interests you. Cut the pictures from the articles and paste them to a piece of cardboard, in an order that tells the story from beginning to end. Write a few paragraphs describing the event.

⊁ 12 RICH AND AMOS

Horatio Alger, a famous writer of the last century, wrote about "rags-to-riches" heroes. His characters always became prosperous by honesty and hard work. So it seems appropriate that Wally Amos should be one of the winners of the Horatio Alger Association awards.

Amos is a real Horatio Alger hero. As a young man in Tallahassee, Florida, he was so poor that he had to walk six miles to learn a trade. He couldn't afford the bus fare.

Today, Amos sells about twelve million dollars worth of his Famous Amos cookies every year. He was the first to open stores that sold only his cookies. Today you can buy his products all over the United States and even in Asia. He is definitely a "rags to riches" hero!

It isn't all hard work, though. Amos is active in literacy programs. He strongly supports efforts to teach people to read and write. But he also wants people to enjoy themselves. "It's okay to have fun while doing important work," he says. He proved his point during a recent meeting to promote literacy by playing "California, Here I Come" on a kazoo.

Perhaps the secret of his success is that Amos enjoys his job. Authorities say that successful people like what they do. Amos certainly likes what he does, and so do lots of other people. Amos received one of the first Presidential Awards for new business excellence from a famous fan, Ronald Reagan.

⌁⌁⌁⌁⌁⌁⌁⌁⌁⌁⌁⌁⌁ UNDERSTANDING THE STORY ⌁⌁⌁⌁⌁⌁⌁⌁⌁⌁⌁⌁

▶ Circle the letter next to each correct statement.

1. The main purpose of this story is to
   a. tell how to make chocolate chip cookies.
   b. tell about a successful and hard working man.
   c. explain how to win awards for hard work.

2. From this story, you can conclude
   a. that Amos did not like a regular job.
   b. that chocolate chip cookies are easy to make.
   c. that people like Amos's chocolate chip cookies.

▶Here are the ten vocabulary words in this lesson. Write them in alphabetical order in the blank spaces below.

prosperous	appropriate	trade	fare	products
definitely	literacy	efforts	authorities	fan

1. _____   6. _____

2. _____   7. _____

3. _____   8. _____

4. _____   9. _____

5. _____   10. _____

wwwwwwwwww **WHAT DO THE WORDS MEAN?** wwwwwwwwww

▶Here are some meanings for the ten vocabulary words in this lesson. Three words have been written beside their meanings. Write the other seven words next to their meanings.

1. _____ attempts

2. _____ proper

3. _____trade_____ job; skill

4. _____ absolutely

5. _____products_____ manufactured items

6. _____ specialists

7. _____ cost of a ticket

8. _____ enthusiastic supporter

9. _____literacy_____ ability to read and write

10. _____ successful

᪥᪥᪥᪥᪥᪥ COMPLETE THE SENTENCES ᪥᪥᪥᪥᪥᪥

▶ **Use the vocabulary words in this lesson to complete the following sentences. Use each word only once. The first one has been done for you.**

prosperous	appropriate	trade	fare	products
definitely	literacy	efforts	authorities	fan

1. Wally Amos _____definitely_____ had a better idea for cookies.

2. He was too poor to pay his bus _____ as a young man.

3. He learned a _____ in Tallahassee, but it wasn't baking cookies.

4. Through his own _____ , he became a wealthy businessman.

5. His baked _____ can be bought in the United States or Asia.

6. Amos believes you can have fun even as you become _____ .

7. So, it seems _____ that he should tell other people to learn how to have fun.

8. Many _____ have studied success and they agree with Amos.

9. Amos also gives time to _____ programs that help others learn to read and write.

10. He can even count a President of the United States as a _____ .

᪥᪥᪥᪥᪥᪥᪥᪥ USE YOUR OWN WORDS ᪥᪥᪥᪥᪥᪥᪥᪥

▶ **Look at this picture. What words come into your mind other than the ten vocabulary words used in this lesson? Write them on the blank lines below. To help you get started, here are two good words.**

1. _____intelligent_____
2. _____busy_____
3. _____
4. _____
5. _____
6. _____
7. _____
8. _____
9. _____
10. _____

▶The *possessive* of a word shows that something belongs to it. For example, Wally has a plan; it is *Wally's* plan. To make a possessive of a word that doesn't end in "s," add an apostrophe and an "s" to the word, such as *cookie's* price or *store's* shelf. To make a possessive of a word that does end in "s," add an apostrophe (') after the "s," such as *cookies'* chips or *stores'* sales. (A proper name ending in "s" is an exception: *Amos's* cookies.) **Here are ten words from the story. In the blank space next to each word, write the correct possessive of the word.**

1. Alger _____

2. heroes _____

3. people _____

4. meeting _____

5. kazoo _____

6. United States _____

7. awards _____

8. Reagan _____

9. winners _____

10. rags _____

▶Here are the ten vocabulary words for this lesson:

prosperous	appropriate	trade	fare	products
definitely	literacy	efforts	authorities	fan

▶There are six blank spaces in the story below. Four vocabulary words have already been used in the story. They are underlined. Use the other six words to fill in the blank spaces.

A _____ businessperson must be ready for hard work. The main idea is to sell the _____ of the business. Success takes great <u>efforts</u> each day. It is _____ not easy. You may get discouraged as you drop your _____ into the bus again and again each day. Yet you should never give up hope!

There are some things you can do to prepare. Reading and writing are important, so work on your _____. The <u>authorities</u> who study business success also say you must be prepared to do things yourself. That is _____ after all, if you want to know how your business works. You can go to <u>trade</u> school to learn some useful business techniques. Read your <u>fan</u> letters. They will tell you what to change and what to leave alone.

╌╌╌╌╌╌╌╌╌╌╌╌╌╌╌╌╌╌ **FOR EXTRA CREDIT** ╌╌╌╌╌╌╌╌╌╌╌╌╌╌╌╌╌╌

Learn More About Business and Products

▶On a separate sheet of paper or in your notebook, do the three exercises below. Then turn them in to your teacher.

1 What product would you like to sell? Write a few sentences explaining the product and why you like it. It does not have to be a food product.

2 Think of places where your product could be sold. Try to be creative. Think of places that no one else has used yet. Explain why each of your choices would be a good place to sell your product.

3 The same word may be used in more than one business. It may have very different meanings in each business. Explain what the words below mean in each of the businesses given.

         1. chips (cookies and computers)
         2. batter (cookies and baseball teams)
         3. sheet (cookies and bedding)
         4. beat (cookies and music)
         5. serve (cookies and tennis)

⌗ 13 A DAYTIME STAR

Oprah Winfrey, the popular actress and talk show host, embodies an important message. That message is: You can be born poor, black, and female and make it to the top.

Oprah spent her first six years with her grandmother, who she says could "whip her for days and never get tired." Oprah says her mother worked hard and wanted the best for her but did not know how to achieve these aims.

As a teenager, Oprah rebelled and got into trouble. She went to Tennessee to live with her father, a strict disciplinarian who encouraged her to read a book each week. Years later, in 1971, Oprah became Miss Black Tennessee. In 1976 she joined the ABC affiliate WJZ-TV in Baltimore as co-newsperson. But it was her film acting that brought her national fame. She won an Academy Award nomination for her role as Sophia in the film of Alice Walker's novel, *The Color Purple*. "Luck," says Oprah, "is a matter of preparation. I've been blessed—but I create the blessings."

Today Oprah Winfrey's name is synonymous with daytime talk shows. She sometimes deals with important social issues on her show. Many people think of her as an activist. Next year she wants to take her show to South Africa. She knows that we still have many racial problems in America. But apartheid in South Africa upsets her more than problems here. Each week millions of Americans watch her shows and care about the issues she presents.

∿∿∿∿∿∿∿∿ UNDERSTANDING THE STORY ∿∿∿∿∿∿∿∿

▶ Circle the letter next to each correct statement.

1. The main idea of this story is that
   a. Oprah Winfrey was nominated for an Academy Award.
   b. despite a poor start in life, Oprah has become very accomplished.
   c. Oprah Winfrey is upset by racial inequality.

2. From the story, you can conclude that
   a. people can overcome difficulties to accomplish what they want.
   b. Oprah will start a new career in South Africa.
   c. children who get beaten will probably never amount to anything.

75

▀▀▀▀▀▀▀▀▀ MAKE AN ALPHABETICAL LIST ▀▀▀▀▀▀▀▀▀

▶ Here are the ten vocabulary words in this lesson. Write them in alphabetical order in the blank spaces below.

issues	affiliate	apartheid	racial	activist
embodies	matter	blessed	synonymous	disciplinarian

1. _____   6. _____

2. _____   7. _____

3. _____   8. _____

4. _____   9. _____

5. _____   10. _____

▀▀▀▀▀▀▀▀▀ WHAT DO THE WORDS MEAN? ▀▀▀▀▀▀▀▀▀

▶ Here are some meanings for the ten vocabulary words in this lesson. Three words have been written beside their meanings. Write the other seven words next to their meanings.

1. _____synonymous_____ alike in meaning or significance

2. _____ a person who believes in strict training

3. _____ a person who publically supports a cause

4. _____affiliate_____ a person or organization connected to a usually larger organization

5. _____ a real thing; content rather than manner or style

6. _____ of, or having to do with race or origins

7. _____ topics or problems under discussion

8. _____ to be given great happiness

9. _____apartheid_____ the governmental policy of racial segregation in South Africa

10. _____ to represent in real or definite form

▶Use the vocabulary words in this lesson to complete the following sentences. Use each word only once. The first one has been done for you.

issues	affiliate	apartheid	racial	activist
embodies	matter	blessed	synonymous	disciplinarian

1. Oprah has become an _____activist_____ for important causes.

2. Her program focuses on important _____ of the day.

3. Oprah really _____ a rags-to-riches story.

4. Oprah's father was a _____ who encouraged education.

5. The TV station Oprah worked for was an _____ of a larger station.

6. Oprah admits that much of her success is a _____ of preparation.

7. Oprah is very aware of the _____ problems in her society.

8. For many viewers, the name Oprah Winfrey is _____ with television talk shows.

9. Oprah says she is _____ because she helps bring about her luck.

10. She is disturbed by _____ in South Africa.

wwwwwwwwwwwww USE YOUR OWN WORDS wwwwwwwwwwwww

▶Look at the picture. What words come into your mind other than the ten vocabulary words in this lesson? Write them on the blank lines below. To help you get started, here are two good words.

1. _____ happy _____

2. _____ successful _____

3. _____

4. _____

5. _____

6. _____

7. _____

8. _____

9. _____

10. _____

DO THE CROSSWORD PUZZLE

▶ In a crossword puzzle, there is a group of boxes, some with numbers in them. There are also two columns of words, or definitions, one for "across" and the other for "down." **Do the puzzle. Each of the words in the puzzle will be one of the vocabulary words in this lesson.**

Across

3. having to do with race

5. strict person

9. public supporter of causes

10. problems

Down

1. a real thing; content

2. makes real

4. given great happiness

6. alike in meaning

7. member

8. South African segregation

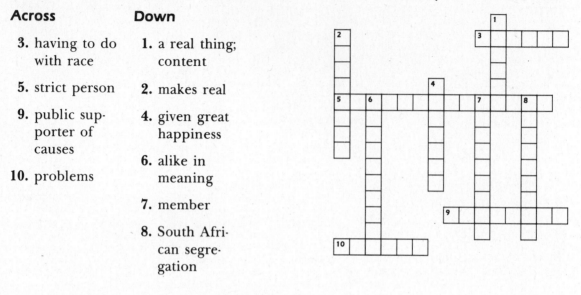

COMPLETE THE STORY

▶ Here are the ten vocabulary words for this lesson:

issue	affiliate	apartheid	racial	activist
embodies	matter	blessed	synonymous	disciplinarian

▶ **There are six blanks in the story below. Two vocabulary words have already been used in the story. They are underlined. Use the other six words to fill in the blank spaces.**

Oprah Winfrey is a successful TV talk show host. She started her career working at an ABC <u>affiliate</u> T.V. station in Baltimore. Oprah considers herself_____, but she knows that much of her luck has been a_____ of work. She has become an <u>activist</u> who is concerned about many important <u>issues</u> of the day. For example, she is very aware of <u>racial</u> discrimination, and so she is against_____ in South Africa. Although her father was a good_____, Oprah had a difficult childhood. Through work and determination she overcame a difficult start to make her name_____ with America's daytime television. Oprah Winfrey_____ the American ideal that through luck and hard work people can succeed against odds.

▰▰▰▰▰▰▰▰▰▰▰▰▰▰ **FOR EXTRA CREDIT** ▰▰▰▰▰▰▰▰▰▰▰▰▰▰

Learn More About Oprah Winfrey

▶**On a separate sheet of paper or in your notebook, do the three exercises below. Then turn them in to your teacher.**

1 Oprah is a leading American television personality. But there are many other black female performers. Choose a dancer, actress, or singer and give some details about that person's life.

2 Oprah Winfrey hosts a popular talk show. On her show, members of the audience sometimes ask questions of the guests. An up-to-date issue is often the topic of the show. Why do you think the show is so popular? Would you like to be in the audience for one of the shows? What topic of discussion would interest you?

3 Oprah Winfrey has lost 67 pounds on a 400-calorie-a-day diet. She now wears a size 8, but she once weighed 200 pounds. Why do you think Oprah wanted to lose weight? Why do you think she was successful? Find out more about Oprah and her weight loss. Check magazines and a book on her diet method to see how she did it.

⅄⅄ 14 FREEDOM FIGHTER ⅄⅄

The stage was bare except for a piano, a bench, and one empty chair. Although the audience sat quietly, a feeling of excitement filled the room. Something great was about to happen.

The houselights dimmed. A short, stout, bald man, carrying a cello and bow in one hand, walked slowly to the chair. He turned and faced the audience. The theater erupted with cheers and wild applause. Pablo Casals, the world's greatest cellist, was about to bring the room alive with his music.

Born in Spain, Pablo Casals became a freedom fighter during the Spanish Revolution. But when the Revolution was over, General Franco had won control over the Spanish people. He formed a dictatorship which restricted the freedom of all the Spanish people. Those who disagreed with him were shot, put in prison, or banished from their homeland. Pablo Casals became a sworn enemy of this tyranny.

Pablo left his native land in protest against Franco's government. But he continued to fight for freedom. He devoted his life to helping the people of Spain. Casals organized benefit concerts in France and Puerto Rico. These music festivals raised money to help Spanish exiles. Pablo was motivated by his love of freedom.

Pablo played from his heart. The music from his stringed instrument was flawless — smooth and moving. When he died in Puerto Rico at the age of 96, he left behind an example for all freedom-loving people of the world.

⌁⌁⌁⌁⌁⌁⌁⌁⌁⌁ UNDERSTANDING THE STORY ⌁⌁⌁⌁⌁⌁⌁⌁⌁⌁

▶ Circle the letter next to each correct statement.

1. Another good title for this story might be:
   a. The World's Greatest Musician
   b. The Dangers of Dictatorship
   c. An Artist Against Tyranny

2. From this story, you can conclude that
   a. people should not mix art with politics.
   b. Pablo Casals gave up his music to fight for freedom.
   c. Pablo Casals took as much pride in his political beliefs as in his music.

▶Here are the ten vocabulary words in this lesson. Write them in alphabetical order in the blank spaces below.

cello	restricted	protest	dictatorship	banished
festivals	motivated	devoted	tyranny	flawless

1. _____   6. _____

2. _____   7. _____

3. _____   8. _____

4. _____   9. _____

5. _____   10. _____

~~~~~~~~~~ WHAT DO THE WORDS MEAN? ~~~~~~~~~~

▶Here are some meanings for the ten vocabulary words in this lesson. Three words have been written beside their meanings. Write the other seven words next to their meanings.

1. _____ stimulated to do something; inspired

2. _____ a musical instrument like a violin, but much larger, that is played in a sitting position

3. _____ limited in freedom or use

4. _____festivals_____ celebrations

5. _____ rule by one person or group that must be obeyed; power held by a few through force

6. _____protest_____ strong objection; opposition

7. _____ perfect; without fault

8. _____banished_____ forced to leave one's country

9. _____ gave up one's time, money, or efforts for some cause or person

10. _____ cruel use of power

▶ Use the vocabulary words in this lesson to complete the following sentences. Use each word only once. The first one has been done for you.

devoted	protest	flawless	banished	festivals
cello	tyranny	dictatorship	motivated	restricted

1. In _____protest_____ against the government of Franco, Pablo Casals left Spain.

2. However, Casals continued to fight against the _____ that limited the freedom of the Spanish people.

3. When freedom of speech is _____ , it is difficult for people to express their true feelings.

4. Those who protest are often _____ from their homeland.

5. The _____ of a dictator causes some people to want to leave.

6. Casals _____ most of his time and energy to organizing benefit concerts.

7. The music _____ he organized succeeded in raising millions of dollars.

8. When people talk about masters of the _____ , Pablo Casals is the name most often mentioned.

9. Casals was _____ by his deep love of music to be a great cellist.

10. His playing was described as _____ and inspiring.

▶ Look at the picture. What words come into your mind other than the ten vocabulary words used in this lesson? Write them on the blank lines below. To help you get started, here are two good words:

1. _____ bow _____
2. _____ strings _____
3. _____
4. _____
5. _____
6. _____
7. _____
8. _____
9. _____
10. _____

~~~~~ MATCH MUSICAL TERMS WITH THEIR MEANINGS ~~~~~

▶ Here are some words selected from the field of music. See if you can match the terms with their meanings.

1. _____ **symphony**   **a.** the speed at which music is played

2. _____ **viola**   **b.** a long musical work for an orchestra

3. _____ **tempo**   **c.** when music gradually becomes louder

4. _____ **tympanist**   **d.** a member of the violin family that is between the violin and cello in size

5. _____ **crescendo**   **e.** the orchestra member who plays the kettledrums

~~~~~ COMPLETE THE STORY ~~~~~

▶ Here are the ten vocabulary words for this lesson:

devoted	dictatorship	motivated	banished	flawless
restricted	cello	festivals	tyranny	protest

▶ There are six blank spaces in the story below. Four vocabulary words have already been used in the story. They are underlined. Use the other six words to fill in the blank spaces.

Pablo Casals, the great _____ master, left his native

Spain in _____ against General Franco's <u>dictatorship</u>.

   Casals was <u>devoted</u> to peace and to helping the people of Spain.

He organized music _____ to raise money for those

Spaniards who had been _____ from their

homeland. In so doing, he _____ other people to

demonstrate against _____.

   Through his _____ music. Casals took a courageous

stand against any government which <u>restricted</u> the freedom of its citizens.

84

▰▰▰▰▰▰▰▰▰▰▰▰▰▰▰▰▰▰▰▰ **FOR EXTRA CREDIT** ▰▰▰▰▰▰▰▰▰▰▰▰▰▰▰▰▰▰▰▰

Learn More About Pablo Casals and Musical Instruments

▶ On a separate sheet of paper or in your notebook, do the three exercises below. Then turn them in to your teacher.

1 Look up some articles which describe Casals playing his cello. Then imagine you are attending one of Casals's concerts as a reporter for your school newspaper. How would you describe the enthusiasm of the audience? How would you describe his playing? Write a paragraph or two in your notebook. Ask your teacher or librarian for help on this exercise.

2 It took a lot of courage for Pablo Casals to become an exile from his home in Spain. If you were exiled, what are some of the things you would miss? Make a list in your notebook.

3 Find some pictures of different instruments that are played in orchestras. Make a scrapbook and label each instrument.

☰ 15 MOUNTAIN OF FIRE ☰

Our bus wound its way slowly up the steep Italian mountainside through olive groves, fruit orchards, and thick forests. At 6,500 feet we reached the end of the road. From this point on we traveled by cable car.

The view below us was unusually beautiful. As far as we could see, the mountain was covered with sand, hardened $\boxed{\text{lava}}$, and ashes. When we reached the end of the cable-car run, we climbed out. It was cold, but we would have to walk the rest of the way.

Our guide said, "This is a very dangerous climb. If anyone falls from the top, he or she will $\boxed{\text{vanish}}$ forever. Therefore, I must $\boxed{\text{enforce}}$ safety rules."

He went on. "An active $\boxed{\text{volcano}}$ is a weak place in the earth's crust. Extremely hot gases $\boxed{\text{exert}}$ tremendous pressure, force their way to the top, and escape from the earth's $\boxed{\text{interior}}$. It can $\boxed{\text{erupt}}$ at any time, sending rivers of molten lava down the mountainside. A few years ago, the village of Santa d'Alfio was destroyed during an eruption. But the brave people rebuilt their town."

We carefully made our way farther up the mountain. When we reached the top, we $\boxed{\text{gingerly}}$ stepped to the edge of the fiery crater, where ropes kept us from getting too close. Clouds of smoke, steam, and black dust rose into the air, causing our eyes to $\boxed{\text{smart}}$. Breathing was difficult. We had reached the $\boxed{\text{peak}}$ of Europe's most active volcano—Mount Etna.

᠁᠁᠁ UNDERSTANDING THE STORY ᠁᠁᠁

▶**Circle the letter next to each correct statement.**

1. The main purpose of this story is to
   a. tell about the violent history of Mount Edna.
   b. provide the reader with information about volcanoes.
   c. describe the adventure of a group of people climbing a volcano

2. If a volcano is said to be active, you can assume that
   a. no one is living in the area around it
   b. scientists are keeping careful watch on it.
   c. it will have a major eruption in the next month.

▶Here are the ten vocabulary words in this lesson. Write them in alphabetical order in the blank spaces below.

enforce	peak	interior	gingerly	erupt
lava	exert	smart	vanish	volcano

1. _____   6. _____

2. _____   7. _____

3. _____   8. _____

4. _____   9. _____

5. _____   10. _____

■■■■■■■■■■ WHAT DO THE WORDS MEAN? ■■■■■■■■■■

▶Here are some meanings for the ten vocabulary words in this lesson. Three words have been written beside their meanings. Write the other seven words next to their meanings.

1. _____smart_____ feel a sharp pain; sting

2. _____ disappear

3. _____ make someone do something; compel

4. _____erupt_____ explode; burst forth

5. _____ inside; inner part

6. _____lava_____ melted rock that comes from a volcano

7. _____ the top; the highest point

8. _____ apply; fully use

9. _____ very carefully

10. _____ a mountain with a cuplike crater which throws out hot melted rock and steam

▶Use the vocabulary words in this lesson to complete the following sentences. Use each word only once. The first one has been done for you.

smart	interior	lava	enforce	volcano
erupt	exert	peak	vanish	gingerly

1. Our eyes began to _____smart_____ from the smoke pouring out of the volcano.

2. The guide said that an active volcano may _____ at any time.

3. Not wanting to "disturb" the volcano, we stepped _____ over the broken pieces of rock.

4. After a long uphill climb, we finally reached the _____ of the volcano.

5. Volcanoes result when forces beneath the earth's surface _____ pressure.

6. Mount Etna is considered to be the most active _____ in Europe today.

7. We wanted to peer into the _____ of the volcano, but the guide warned us not to get that close.

8. Police _____ laws that prohibit people from getting close to the volcano.

9. The _____ streaming down the mountainside looked like a river of fire.

10. Whole villages have been known to _____ from sight after an eruption.

========= USE YOUR OWN WORDS =========

▶Look at the picture. What words come into your mind other than the ten vocabulary words used in this lesson? Write them on the blank lines below. To help you get started, here are two good words:

1. _____smoke_____

2. _____heat_____

3. _____

4. _____

5. _____

6. _____

7. _____

8. _____

9. _____

10. _____

▶There are six vocabulary words listed below. To the right of each is either a synonym or an antonym. Remember, a **synonym** is a word that means the same, or nearly the same, as another word. An **antonym** is a word that means the opposite of another word. **On the line beside each pair of words, write S for synonyms or A for antonyms. The first one has been done for you.**

1. vanish	appear	1.	A
2. peak	bottom	2.	
3. smart	sting	3.	
4. gingerly	carelessly	4.	
5. interior	exterior	5.	
6. erupt	gush	6.	

~~~~~~ COMPLETE THE STORY ~~~~~~

▶**Here are the ten vocabulary words for this lesson:**

enforce	peak	interior	gingerly	erupt
lava	exert	smart	vanish	volcano

▶**There are six blank spaces in the story below. Four vocabulary words have already been used in the story. They are underlined. Use the other six words to fill in the blank spaces.**

A <u>volcano</u> is active when the <u>interior</u> gases can push their way upward to the surface. An active volcano can produce rivers of molten

_____ .

A volcano is inactive if it cannot_____ .

One must_____ caution when visiting an active volcano. You must step <u>gingerly</u> around the crater. Careless people have been known to fall into the crater and suddenly

_____ . To prevent such accidents, officials

_____ strict safety regulations.

While on the <u>peak</u> of an active volcano, a visitor might have to use a handkerchief to cover his or her mouth. The gases can burn your throat and make your eyes_____ .

Learn More About Volcanoes

▶ **On a separate sheet of paper or in your notebook, do the three exercises below. Then turn them in to your teacher.**

1   If you were a guide on Mount Etna, what would be the most important thing for you to remember? Give reasons.

2   Write a short paragraph listing five of the world's active volcanoes. Do not include Mount Etna. Explain where each volcano is located, and tell when it last erupted.

3   Look up the eruption of Mount Vesuvius in Pompeii, Italy, in A. D. 79. Read about it, especially what happened to the city. Then pretend you are a news reporter telling the rest of the world about the eruption. Remember, you've just witnessed these events. Write a few paragraphs describing what happened.

16 GOING ONCE, GOING TWICE...

The proud colt steps into the auction ring. He is turned in slow circles. His brown coat has been brushed to a high gloss . The horse breeders study the thoroughbred. The auctioneer begins his chant . The bidding starts at a quarter of a million dollars. Quickly, the price rises to half a million. Breeders from many different countries compete against one another. The final bid is one and a half million dollars. The colt now has an owner.

The Keeneland racecourse in Kentucky is the scene of many multi-million-dollar bids. Buyers look for a horse with an excellent pedigree . In this way they improve the bloodlines of their stables.

One likely colt sold for four and a half million dollars. He was the son of the great racehorse Nijinsky II. Even more amazing are the prices paid when groups of people buy horses jointly . In shared ownership, each partner has the right to breed the horse once a year. Conquistador Cielo was bought this way for over 36 million dollars! His owners hoped he would sire many winners.

Splendid banquets are given to attract horse buyers to auctions. These banquets have become a permanent part of the auction scene. In addition to enjoying themselves, buyers study each horse carefully. Future owners investigate every aspect of a horse before bidding. They even use computers to trace bloodlines. Buying racehorses is no small matter. Going once, going twice, . . . sold!

~~~~~~~~~~~~~~ UNDERSTANDING THE STORY ~~~~~~~~~~~~~~

▶Circle the letter next to each correct statement.

1. The main idea of this story is that
   a. huge sums of money are spent at auctions on horses that can win races and sire other great racehorses.
   b. buying horses jointly helps breeders to afford them.
   c. the use of computers in tracing bloodlines has revolutionized the business of buying racehorses.

2. From this story, you can conclude that
   a. the record price paid for Conquistador Cielo will not seem high in years to come.
   b. thoroughbreds will soon be inexpensive because there will be so many of them.
   c. a flowing mane and large front hooves are signs of a great racehorse.

▶ Here are the ten vocabulary words in this lesson. Write them in alphabetical order in the blank spaces below.

gloss	auctioneer	compete	sire	chant
permanent	jointly	investigate	banquets	pedigree

1. _____   6. _____

2. _____   7. _____

3. _____   8. _____

4. _____   9. _____

5. _____   10. _____

░░░░░░░░░░ WHAT DO THE WORDS MEAN? ░░░░░░░░░░

▶ Here are some meanings for the ten vocabulary words in this lesson. Three words have been written beside their meanings. Write the other seven words next to their meanings.

1. _____ oppose; try for the same thing

2. _____ agent in charge of selling at an auction

3. _____banquets_____ formal meals; lavish feasts

4. _____ high polish; shine

5. _____investigate_____ study; look into carefully

6. _____ together; in partnership

7. _____ be the father of

8. _____ rapid and rhythmic speaking

9. _____pedigree_____ record of an animal's ancestors, especially with respect to purity of breed

10. _____ lasting; continuing

94

˙˙˙˙˙˙˙˙˙˙˙˙˙˙˙ COMPLETE THE SENTENCES ˙˙˙˙˙˙˙˙˙˙˙˙˙˙˙

▶Use the vocabulary words in this lesson to complete the following sentences. Use each word only once. The first one has been done for you.

chant	auctioneer	permanent	gloss	pedigree
investigate	jointly	banquets	compete	sire

1. When the _____auctioneer_____ banged her gravel on the stand, it meant the sale was over.

2. The auctioneer's _____ sounded like a tuneless song.

3. Great _____ are served at horse auctions in order to attract bidders.

4. The tension in the room rises as breeders _____ against one another.

5. A breeder will always _____ a horse's health and bloodline before bidding.

6. A breeder wants to be sure that the _____ of a horse is a good one.

7. Buyers sometimes get together and purchase a horse _____ .

8. A good diet and daily brushing give a high _____ to a horse's coat.

9. A horse can _____ many young, but only a few may grow up to be great racehorses.

10. A famous racehorse often becomes a _____ part of a well-known stable.

˙˙˙˙˙˙˙˙˙˙˙˙˙˙˙ USE YOUR OWN WORDS ˙˙˙˙˙˙˙˙˙˙˙˙˙˙˙

▶Look at the picture. What words come into your mind other than the ten vocabulary words used in this lesson? Write them on the blank lines below. To help you get started, here are two good words:

1. _____bidder_____
2. _____ropes_____
3. _____
4. _____
5. _____
6. _____
7. _____
8. _____
9. _____
10. _____

IDENTIFY THE SYNONYMS AND ANTONYMS

▶There are six vocabulary words listed below. To the right of each is either a synonym or an antonym. Remember, a *synonym* is a word that means the same, or nearly the same, as another word. An *antonym* is a word that means the opposite of another word. **On the line beside each pair of words, write *S* for synonyms or *A* for antonyms. The first one has been done for you.**

1. compete   cooperate   _____A_____

2. pedigree   history   _____

3. jointly   separately   _____

4. banquets   meals   _____

5. permanent   temporary   _____

6. auctioneer   buyer   _____

COMPLETE THE STORY

▶Here are the ten vocabulary words for this lesson:

compete	gloss	pedigree	auctioneer	chant
sire	banquets	investigate	permanent	jointly

▶There are six blank spaces in the story below. Four vocabulary words have already been used in the story. They are underlined. Use the other six words to fill in the blank spaces.

Horse auctions are exciting. The horses' coats are brushed to a high _____ . The _____ leads the show with a <u>chant</u> that is rapid and singsong. Tasty and attractive _____ are served to bring in buyers. These feasts have become a _____ part of the scene.

You can be sure that buyers _____ every detail of a horse's history before bidding. The <u>pedigree</u> is studied to see how many of the horse's ancestors were winners. The breeders <u>compete</u> for horses with excellent records.

Because racehorses are so costly, people often decide to buy them _____ . They hope that the horse will <u>sire</u> many great racers.

96

Learn More About Owning and Racing Horses

▶On a separate sheet of paper or in your notebook, do the three exercises below. Then turn them in to your teacher.

1 What do you think would be the advantages to using computers to trace bloodlines? List at least four advantages. Remember to consider such factors as time, accuracy, and ability to compare information.

2 Owning horses is a costly business. The horses have to be cared for and trained. Research this topic in the library. Write a short paragraph describing the expenses involved. You may even want to figure out the average cost in dollars and cents of owning one of these fine animals.

3 Have you ever watched the thoroughbreds race? The Preakness and the Kentucky Derby are two very famous races that are shown on TV. Imagine that you are an announcer for one of these races. Describe the events in a short paragraph.

17

THE MYSTERY OF STONEHENGE

One of the most mysterious places in the world is Stonehenge, in England. Here an ancient monument of rock dominates the landscape.

At Stonehenge there are three circles of huge stones, one inside the other. Each stone is approximately 14 feet high and weighs about 28 tons. Next to each stone in the outer circle is a shallow pit. Inside the smallest circle are stones shaped like horseshoes. At the center is a fallen stone that could have been an altar.

The rocks of Stonehenge still perplex scientists today. Carvings on the stones denote they were put there about 4,000 years ago. Some pundits believe Stonehenge was built for sun worship. Others say it might have been built by pagan priests as a temple or a burial place. Cremated bodies have been found in the pits. Still other people believe Stonehenge was an astronomical calendar used to tell the seasons of the year and eclipses of the sun and moon.

There are also many questions about how the stones got there. Were they hauled overland or floated on rafts? How were they raised to an upright position?

No one has been able to answer these questions. Stonehenge remains one of the world's biggest mysteries.

⚞⚞⚞⚞⚞⚞⚞ UNDERSTANDING THE STORY ⚞⚞⚞⚞⚞⚞⚞

▶ **Circle the letter next to each correct statement.**

1. The main idea of this story is that
   a. most scientists believe Stonehenge was an astronomical calendar.
   b. the origin of Stonehenge remains a mystery although many theories have been suggested.
   c. Stonehenge is considered one of the seven wonders of the world.

2. The fact that human ashes were found in the pits at Stonehenge suggests that
   a. the area was used as a battlefield.
   b. the stones are what is left of a larger structure that burned to the ground.
   c. bodies were often cremated before burial in ancient times.

►Here are the ten vocabulary words in this lesson. Write them in alphabetical order in the blank spaces below.

monument	approximately	denote	pagan	astronomical
burial	perplex	pundits	cremated	eclipses

1. _____
2. _____
3. _____
4. _____
5. _____

6. _____
7. _____
8. _____
9. _____
10. _____

WHAT DO THE WORDS MEAN?

►Here are some meanings for the ten vocabulary words in this lesson. Three words have been written beside their meanings. Write the other seven words next to their meanings.

1. _____ burnt to ashes

2. _____pundits_____ persons who have knowledge of a subject

3. _____ puzzle; confuse

4. _____ show; point out

5. _____ times when the sun or moon cannot be seen because its light is blocked

6. _____monument_____ something from a past age that is believed to have historical importance

7. _____astronomical_____ having to do with astronomy, or the study of planets, stars, and other bodies in outer space

8. _____ a follower of a religion with many gods

9. _____ having to do with placing a body in its final resting place

10. _____ nearly; about

▶Use the vocabulary words in this lesson to complete the following sentences. Use each word only once. The first one has been done for you.

pundits	denote	eclipses	astronomical	burial
monument	cremated	pagan	perplex	approximately

1. A question that continues to _____perplex_____ scientists is what was the purpose of Stonehenge.

2. Predicting _____ of the sun and moon may have been the original purpose.

3. In fact, drawings of ancient _____ calendars show structures that look much like Stonehenge.

4. Priests of a _____ religion may have meant the stones to be a temple.

5. Carvings on the stones _____ that Stonehenge is about 4,000 years old.

6. One of the things that _____ wonder is how the huge stones were moved from Wales to England.

7. The ashes of _____ bodies were found in the area of the outer circle.

8. That Stonehenge was a sacred _____ place is indicated by these ashes.

9. A wall of earth _____ 320 feet (98 m) in diameter surrounds the stones.

10. The _____ of Stonehenge stands as a reminder of ancient people.

▶Look at the picture. What words come into your mind other than the ten vocabulary words used in this lesson? Write them on the blank lines below. To help you get started, here are two good words:

1. _____grass_____
2. _____sky_____
3. _____
4. _____
5. _____
6. _____
7. _____
8. _____
9. _____
10. _____

▶In an **analogy**, similar relationships occur between words that are different. For example, *pig* is to *hog*, as *car* is to *automobile*. The relationship is that the words mean the same. Here's another analogy: *noisy* is to *quiet* as *short* is to *tall*. In this relationship, the words have opposite meanings.

▶See if you can complete the following analogies. Circle the correct word or words.

1. **Denote** is to **point out** as **dominates** is to
   a. rises above.   **b.** towers over.   **c.** grows up.   **d.** climbs over.

2. **Stonehenge** is to **monument** as **eclipses** is to
   a. sunlight   **b.** planets   **c.** heavenly bodies   **d.** blackouts

3. **Mysterious** is to **strange** as **ancient** is to
   a. approximately   **b.** old   **c.** pagan   **d.** astronomical

4. **Perplex** is to **confuse** as **cremated** is to
   a. boiled   **b.** buried   **c.** cooled   **d.** burnt

5. **Erected** is to **destroyed** as **upright** is to
   a. fallen   **b.** vertical   **c.** approximately   **d.** astronomical

wwwwwwwwwwww COMPLETE THE STORY wwwwwwwwwwww

▶Here are the ten vocabulary words for this lesson:

monument	perplex	pundits	cremated	eclipses
approximately	denote	pagan	astronomical	burial

▶There are six blank spaces in the story below. Four vocabulary words have already been used in the story. They are underlined. Use the other six words to fill the blank spaces.

The rock _____ of Stonehenge dominates the Salisbury Plains in England.

The rocks of Stonehenge still _____ pundits today. Some believe Stonehenge was an _____ calendar that predicted eclipses of the moon and sun. Others think it was used as a _____ temple or _____ place. Cremated bodies have been found there. Carvings denote the stones were erected _____ 4,000 years ago.

Despite modern science, Stonehenge remains a mystery.

102

~~~~~ FOR EXTRA CREDIT ~~~~~

Learn More About Stonehenge

▶On a separate sheet of paper or in your notebook, do the three exercises below. Then turn them in to your teacher.

1 The following names and terms are connected with Stonehenge. Choose three and look them up in an encyclopedia or other books in the library. Find out who or what each one is. How is each related to Stonehenge?

Aubrey Holes	sarsen	Gerald Hawkins
John Aubrey	Salisbury Plains	

2 Who or what were the Druids? Find out as much as you can about them.

3 Scholars have wondered for years how the stones were brought to Stonehenge and where the stones came from. What are your thoughts on this subject? Write a story describing how you feel the stones got to Stonehenge. Let your imagination take over. Be creative!

18

AN ARTIST TRUE TO HER OWN VISION

As a child, Georgia O'Keeffe showed a talent for art. She enjoyed expressing her feelings in images. One day, Alfred Stieglitz, a famous critic and photographer, saw some of her work. He liked it so much he exhibited her paintings in a one-woman show. That show, in 1916, made O'Keeffe's reputation as an important artist. She married Stieglitz, and he encouraged her to express her vision in her own way. Giant flowers, barns, sharply drawn buildings, and bright landscapes emerged from her brush.

O'Keeffe's paintings display freshness and vigor. Her works vary a great deal. This makes classification of her style difficult. Some critics label her a romanticist. Others say she is a realist.

O'Keeffe moved to New Mexico. Rural, or country, scenes appealed to her. She found them preferable to urban, or city, subjects. Canyons, adobe houses, and vast landscapes of the Southwest appeared in many of her paintings. She painted a skull ornamented with a bright flower to show life and death together. Some of her paintings became dreamy and impressionistic. Others were sharp and clear.

Georgia O'Keeffe died in 1986, and her popularity continues to increase. In 1989, an O'Keeffe retrospective was exhibited in major museums across the country, an honor reserved for the best artists.

~~~~~~~~~~~~~~~ UNDERSTANDING THE STORY ~~~~~~~~~~~~~~~

▶**Circle the letter next to each correct statement.**

1. The main idea of this story is that
   a. Georgia O'Keeffe was married to the famous critic and photographer Alfred Stieglitz.
   b. the variety and vigor of O'Keeffe's painting place her among the best artists of this century.
   c. O'Keeffe's paintings usually show rural rather than urban scenes.

2. From this story, you can conclude that
   a. the American Academy of Arts and Letters elected O'Keeffe a member on the basis of her skull paintings alone.
   b. O'Keeffe's career as a painter ended when she married Stieglitz.
   c. O'Keeffe's paintings present her personal vision of life in a way that appeals to many people.

▶ Here are the ten vocabulary words in this lesson. Write them in alphabetical order in the blank spaces below.

| retrospective | exhibited | classification | rural | vigor |
| romanticist | vast | ornamented | preferable | impressionistic |

1. _____   6. _____

2. _____   7. _____

3. _____   8. _____

4. _____   9. _____

5. _____   10. _____

WHAT DO THE WORDS MEAN?

▶ Here are some meanings for the ten vocabulary words in this lesson. Three words have been written beside their meanings. Write the other seven words next to their meanings.

1. _____ putting something into a special group or class

2. _____ displayed; shown to the public

3. _____ preferable _____ something liked better; more desirable

4. _____ huge; spacious

5. _____ vigor _____ strength; vitality

6. _____ an exhibition of the life-time work of an artist

7. _____ having to do with open country and farming

8. _____ decorated; made more beautiful

9. _____ romanticist _____ one who paints people and things as she or he would like them to be rather than as they really are

10. _____ in the style of painting in which the painter tries to catch a momentary glimpse of the subject

106

▶ Use the vocabulary words in this lesson to complete the following sentences. Use each word only once. The first one has been done for you.

vigor	preferable	impressionistic	rural	retrospective
classification	vast	romanticist	ornamented	exhibited

1. ___Impressionistic___ painters try to capture the effect of sunlight in their paintings.

2. _____ of O'Keeffe's work is hard because different styles appear in it.

3. A _____ is likely to paint landscapes that have a certain ideal beauty.

4. O'Keeffe was a young, unknown artist when Stieglitz _____ her work.

5. The brush strokes in O'Keeffe's paintings show _____ and spirit.

6. The _____ lands of New Mexico greatly impressed O'Keeffe.

7. Though most of her paintings are simple, some are _____ with brightly colored leaves and flowers.

8. As a child, O'Keeffe found it _____ to express herself in painted images.

9. After her death, many museums displayed the O'Keeffe _____ which toured the country.

10. Houses made of adobe are common in the _____ Southwest.

▶ Look at the picture. What words come into your mind other than the ten vocabulary words used in this lesson? Write them on the blank lines below. To help you get started, here are two good words:

1. ___work___

2. ___shapes___

3. _____

4. _____

5. _____

6. _____

7. _____

8. _____

9. _____

10. _____

107

▶ The story you read has many interesting words that were not highlighted as vocabulary words. Six of these words are *vary, scene, critic, express, talent,* and *vision.* Can you think of a synonym for each of these words? Remember, a **synonym** is a word that means the same, or nearly the same, as another word. *Sorrowful* and *sad* are synonyms. **Write the synonym in the blank space next to the word.**

1. vary _____

2. scene _____

3. critic _____

4. express _____

5. talent _____

6. vision _____

━━━━━━━━ **COMPLETE THE STORY** ━━━━━━━━

▶ **Here are the ten vocabulary words for this lesson:**

retrospective	classification	preferable	ornamented	rural
vigor	impressionistic	romanticist	vast	exhibited

▶ **There are six blank spaces in the story below. Four vocabulary words have already been used in the story. They are underlined. Use the other six words to fill in the blank spaces.**

When Alfred Stieglitz first_____ the works of

Georgia O'Keeffe, the critics were amazed. They found it hard to

believe that this artist painted so well in so many styles. Classification

of her paintings into one group seemed impossible. Some viewers

thought her art was_____ in style. Others said that

she was a romanticist in her outlook. She soon achieved a reputation

as one of the finest artists in the United States.

O'Keeffe's paintings show a vigor that is inspiring. The dried bones

and_____ deserts she paints are often brightly

_____ with huge flowers or plants. While urban

artists find it preferable to paint city scenes, her works show scenes

of_____ life. People could see examples of her dif-

ferent styles in the_____ displayed after her death.

‧‧‧‧‧‧‧‧‧‧‧‧‧‧‧‧‧‧‧‧‧‧‧‧‧ **FOR EXTRA CREDIT** ‧‧‧‧‧‧‧‧‧‧‧‧‧‧‧‧‧‧‧‧‧‧‧

Learn More About the Southwest, Art, and Artists

▶On a separate piece of paper or in your notebook, do the three exercises below. Then turn them in to your teacher.

1 Look through magazines such as *Life* and *National Geographic*. Cut out
any pictures that you find of the land and people of the southwestern United
States. Look especially for pictures of deserts, mountains, canyons, and
adobe houses. Paste these pictures to a large piece of cardboard or put
them on the bulletin board in your classroom.

2 There are many women artists of great talent. Here are the names
of a few:

Mary Cassatt	Judy Chicago
Suzanne Valadon	Louise Nevelson
Lee Krasner	Käthe Kollwitz

Go to the library and look through books that contain their works. Select
one artist and write a paragraph or two about her life and work. Be a
critic—tell why you do or do not like her work.

3 Go to the library and find a book that contains photographs by Alfred
Stieglitz. Choose one photo and write a paragraph about it. It may be one
of Georgia O'Keeffe or any other subject. In your paragraph, try to answer the following questions: What does the photo show? How does it make
you feel? What do you think Stieglitz was thinking or feeling when he took
it?

19

THE PROUD TOWER OF PARIS

When one thinks of famous structures of the world, the Eiffel Tower comes to mind. This breathtaking landmark rises 984 feet above Paris. It offers a grand panorama of the city.

A visitor can take an elevator to any of the tower's three observation floors. From each platform the camera bug can take pictures of the city. These photos will surely become treasured souvenirs . The visitor gets a splendid view of the Cathedral of Notre Dame, the Seine River, and the Louvre, one of the world's leading art museums. Binoculars are available for closeup viewing of these great sights.

The tower was designed by the man for whom it was named— Alexandre Gustave Eiffel. It was built for an exposition in 1889. Nothing like it had ever been built before. It was constructed in less than a year at small cost. The Eiffel Tower remained the tallest building in the world for 41 years. (The Chrysler Building in New York topped it in 1930.)

There is a restaurant on the first floor of the tower. Here the visitor can hear expressions of wonder in many languages. Tourists from all over the world make a point of visiting the tower.

For the tourist from any nation, the memories of visiting the Eiffel Tower will endure forever.

UNDERSTANDING THE STORY

▶ Circle the letter next to each correct statement.

1. The main purpose of this story is to
   a. list the many historic landmarks in Paris.
   b. describe probably the most famous landmark in Paris.
   c. tell of the struggles Alexandre Gustave Eiffel had in building the tower.

2. From this story, you can conclude that
   a. the Eiffel Tower is taller than the World Trade Center in New York City.
   b. Paris is the most popular city in Europe.
   c. the loss of the Eiffel Tower would be a serious blow to French tourism.

▶Here are the ten vocabulary words in this lesson. Write them in alphabetical order in the blank spaces below.

| exposition | landmark | souvenirs | breathtaking | endure |
| platform | panorama | expressions | structures | binoculars |

1. _____   6. _____

2. _____   7. _____

3. _____   8. _____

4. _____   9. _____

5. _____   10. _____

~~~~~~~~~~~ **WHAT DO THE WORDS MEAN?** ~~~~~~~~~~~

▶Here are some meanings for the ten vocabulary words in this lesson. Three words have been written beside their meanings. Write the other seven words next to their meanings.

1. _____ a wide view of a surrounding region

2. _____breathtaking_____ very exciting; thrilling

3. _____ sounds or actions which show some feelings

4. _____ a raised level surface

5. _____structures_____ things that are built, such as buildings or towers

6. _____ something familiar or easily seen

7. _____ glasses used to magnify faraway objects

8. _____exposition_____ public show or exhibition

9. _____ things bought or kept for remembrance

10. _____ last; keep on

112

wwwwwwwwwww **COMPLETE THE SENTENCES** wwwwwwwwwww

▶Use the vocabulary words in this lesson to complete the following sentences. Use each word only once. The first one has been done for you.

souvenirs	expressions	platform	exposition	endure
binoculars	structures	breathtaking	panorama	landmark

1. At an _____exposition_____ products of science, industry, and art are displayed.

2. Among the well-known _____ in Paris, the Eiffel Tower is the most famous.

3. Just as the Washington Monument is a national _____ in the U.S., the Eiffel Tower is one in France.

4. The view from the observation deck is _____ .

5. This deck serves as an ideal _____ from which to take pictures.

6. Her parents returned with _____ from their tour of Europe.

7. Many tourists carry _____ with them so they can get closeup views.

8. You can hear _____ of pleasure from visitors to the Louvre as their eyes fall upon the beautiful paintings.

9. For a _____ of New York City, go to the top of the World Trade Center.

10. In order to make the Eiffel Tower _____ , it is well cared for.

wwwwwwwwwww **USE YOUR OWN WORDS** wwwwwwwwwww

▶Look at the picture. What words come into your mind other than the ten vocabulary words used in this lesson? Write them on the blank lines below. To help you get started, here are two good words:

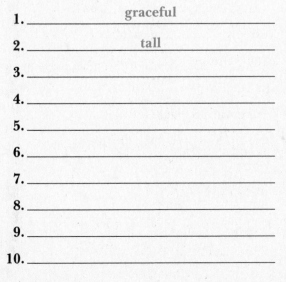

1. _____graceful_____
2. _____tall_____
3. _____
4. _____
5. _____
6. _____
7. _____
8. _____
9. _____
10. _____

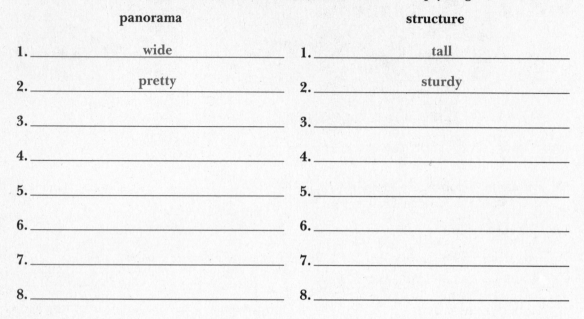

DESCRIBE THE NOUNS

▶ Two of our vocabulary words, *panorama* and *structure*, are nouns. List as many words as you can which describe or tell something about the words *panorama* and *structure*. You can work on this with your classmates. Listed below are some words to help you get started.

panorama

1. _____ wide _____
2. _____ pretty _____
3. _____
4. _____
5. _____
6. _____
7. _____
8. _____

structure

1. _____ tall _____
2. _____ sturdy _____
3. _____
4. _____
5. _____
6. _____
7. _____
8. _____

COMPLETE THE STORY

▶ Here are the ten vocabulary words for this lesson:

breathtaking	souvenirs	exposition	expressions	endure
landmark	panorama	platform	binoculars	structures

▶ There are six blank spaces in the story below. Four vocabulary words have already been used in the story. They are underlined. Use the other six words to fill in the blank spaces.

When the Eiffel Tower was built for an _____ back

in 1889, it was the highest of all <u>structures</u> in Paris. Today this

_____ is still one of the wonders of the world.

Many _____ of wonder have been used to

describe the tower's view. Indeed, the observation decks offer a

breathtaking _____ of the city. A visitor can take

a close look by using _____ .

Tourists may take advantage of a restaurant on the bottom

<u>platform</u> and a stand where they may purchase _____ .

The Eiffel Tower will continue to <u>endure</u> as one of the world's pre-

mier attractions.

114

Learn More About People, Places, and Things

▶ On a separate sheet of paper or in your notebook, do the three exercises below. Then turn them in to your teacher.

1 Find out more about the man who designed the Eiffel Tower—Alexandre Gustave Eiffel. Then write a short paragraph giving some details of his life and work. What famous statue in New York City did he help to design?

2 If you were asked to design the world's tallest building, what would it look like? What would the building be used for? In what city or country might you build it? What name would you give it? Write a brief description of your world's tallest building. Be creative!

3 Paris has many fascinating and beautiful landmarks. What are some of them? Look in an encyclopedia and make a list of at least five Parisian landmarks.

20 A STRING SENSATION

On a **humid** summer night in 1986, Midori prepared to take a bow. The fourteen-year-old violinist was **stunned** by what happened next. The entire audience cheered, stomped, and whistled wildly. Then the **conductor** and musicians of the Boston Symphony **Orchestra** hugged and kissed her.

The young concert violinist had just played Leonard Bernstein's *Serenade.* Her performance was "technically near-perfect." But that was only part of the story. Near the end of this long, **elaborate** piece, one of the strings on her violin snapped. Without missing a beat, she borrowed the concertmaster's violin and continued. Then, unbelievably, another string broke. Again she switched violins and continued playing. The new violins were larger than the one this **diminutive** girl was used to. But Midori finished the concert. She later explained, "I didn't want to stop. I love that piece."

Japanese-born Midori Goto was a child **prodigy**. At age ten, Midori was accepted by the **renowned** Juilliard School in New York. She went on to play with some of the world's best-known violinists.

But on that magical night in 1986, Midori's whole life changed. She became famous. Yet, Midori remained an **unaffected** teenager. While on tour, she still liked to **frolic** with her Snoopy doll.

When asked about her plans for the future, Midori said, "I think I'll be a writer, or an architect—or maybe a violinist." To the thousands of people who have heard her perform, the choice is clear.

UNDERSTANDING THE STORY

▶Circle the letter next to each correct statement.

1. The main idea of this story is that
   a. Midori switched violins twice during the Tanglewood Festival.
   b. Midori has performed with some of the best-known violinists in the world.
   c. Midori has proven to be a talented violinist and a determined young lady who enjoys life.

2. From this story, you can conclude that
   a. Midori will not give up easily.
   b. Midori will continue to break violin strings during her concerts.
   c. Midori will return to the Juilliard School.

▶Here are the ten vocabulary words in this lesson. Write them in alphabetical order in the blank spaces below.

elaborate	orchestra	diminutive	stunned	humid
frolic	unaffected	conductor	prodigy	renowned

1. _____   6. _____

2. _____   7. _____

3. _____   8. _____

4. _____   9. _____

5. _____   10. _____

~~~~~~~~~ WHAT DO THE WORDS MEAN? ~~~~~~~~~

▶Here are some meanings for the ten vocabulary words in this lesson. Three words have been written beside their meanings. Write the other seven words next to their meanings.

1. _____ the leader of a group of musicians

2. _____ very small, tiny

3. _____unaffected_____ not influenced or changed; natural

4. _____ musicians who perform together, especially on stringed instruments

5. _____renowned_____ having a great reputation; famous

6. _____ complicated; intricate

7. _____ damp, moist air

8. _____prodigy_____ a highly gifted or talented person, usually a child

9. _____ made senseless, dizzy; confused

10. _____ to play about happily

◆◆◆◆◆◆◆◆◆◆ COMPLETE THE SENTENCES ◆◆◆◆◆◆◆◆◆◆

▶Use the vocabulary words in this lesson to complete the following sentences. Use each word only once. The first one has been done for you.

elaborate	renowned	prodigy	stunned	orchestra
unaffected	frolic	humid	diminutive	conductor

1. We don't expect to see famous musicians _____frolic_____ with a doll.

2. It is difficult to perform on a hot and _____ night.

3. Teachers at the Juilliard School knew Midori was a _____ .

4. Midori was _____ when the other musicians hugged and kissed her.

5. Midori, like all musicians, had to follow the lead of the _____ .

6. Her performance at Tanglewood proved that Midori deserved to be _____ .

7. Midori looked especially _____ next to the taller musicians.

8. A musician must practice often to play a _____ piece like *Serenade*.

9. Midori's friends are glad that, in spite of her fame, she is still _____ .

10. Members of the _____ were proud to be part of Midori's special night.

◆◆◆◆◆◆◆◆◆◆ USE YOUR OWN WORDS ◆◆◆◆◆◆◆◆◆◆

▶Look at the picture. What words come into your mind other than the ten vocabulary words used in this lesson? Write them on the blank lines below. To help you get started, here are two good words:

1. _____performer_____
2. _____violin_____
3. _____
4. _____
5. _____
6. _____
7. _____
8. _____
9. _____
10. _____

▶The story you read has many interesting words that were not highlighted as vocabulary words. Six of these words are *wildly, performance, snapped, switched, entire,* and *completed.* Can you think of a synonym for each of these words? Remember, a synonym is a word that means the same, or nearly the same, as another word. *Happy* and *glad* are synonyms. **Write the synonym on the blank space next to the word.**

1. wildly _____

2. performance _____

3. snapped _____

4. switched _____

5. entire _____

6. completed _____

wwwwwwwwwwwww COMPLETE THE STORY wwwwwwwwwwwww

▶Here are the ten vocabulary words for this lesson:

elaborate	orchestra	renowned	conductor	stunned
unaffected	frolic	humid	diminutive	prodigy

▶**There are six blank spaces in the story below. Four vocabulary words have already been used in the story. They are underlined. Use the other six words to fill in the blank spaces.**

Midori's parents knew their child was a <u>prodigy</u>. Yet even they must

have been _____ by her performance at Tanglewood.

The <u>conductor</u> hugged and kissed her. So did the musicians in

the _____ . They all realized that the hot and

_____ weather made it hard to perform. They also

realized that the music was long and _____ . How

difficult this experience must have been for the <u>diminutive</u> girl!

Midori surely deserves to be _____ . But she never

felt too important to _____ like a child. Who could

have expected her to remain so <u>unaffected</u> after all that attention?

╼╼╼╼╼╼╼╼╼╼╼╼╼╼╼╼ **FOR EXTRA CREDIT** ╼╼╼╼╼╼╼╼╼╼╼╼╼╼╼╼

Learn More About Midori and Her Achievements

▶On a separate sheet of paper or in your notebook, do the three exercises below. Then turn them in to your teacher.

1 Pretend you were in the audience for Midori's performance at the Tanglewood Festival. Write a few sentences describing what you saw. Explain how it made you feel. You may want to go to the library to get more information about that "magical night."

2 Midori was fourteen years old when she gave the performance that changed her life. What has she done since Tanglewood? What is she doing now? Research these questions at your local library. Write a paragraph or two telling what you have found.

3 When faced with a difficult situation, Midori refused to quit. Do you know someone who was determined to succeed? Write a few paragraphs about a person you know or have read about who refused to give up. How you would have acted in this situation?

A

activist [AK tiv ist] a person who publicly supports a cause

additives [AD duh tivz] a substance added to change or improve a natural product

admirers [ad MYR urz] those who respect or have high opinions

affiliate [af FIL ee it] a person or organization connected to a usually larger organization

altered [AWL turd] changed

apartheid [uh PAHRT ayt] the governmental policy of racial segregation in South Africa

apparatus [ap uh RAT us] materials, tools, special instruments, or machinery needed to carry out a purpose

apparel [uh PAIR ul] clothing; dress

apply [uh PLY] seek a job; ask for work

appropriate [uh PRO pree it] proper

approximately [uh PROK suh mit lee] nearly; about

aptitude [AP tuh tood] natural ability or capacity; talent

arrested [uh REST ed] held by the police

articulate [ahr TIK yuh layt] to express in clear verbal form

assignments [uh SYN munts] definite tasks or jobs to be done; specific works to be accomplished

astronomical [as truh NOM uh kul] having to do with astronomy, or the study of planets, stars, and other bodies in outer space

attained [uh TAYND] reached; achieved

auctioneer [AWK shun eer] agent in charge of selling at an auction

authorities [uh THOR ih teez] specialists

B

banished [BAN isht] forced to leave one's country

banquets [BAN kwits] formal meals; lavish feasts

binoculars [buh NOK yuh lurz] glasses used to magnify faraway objects

blessed [BLES id] to be given great happiness

bolted [BOHL tid] fastened; held with metal fittings

breathtaking [BRETH tayk ing] very exciting; thrilling

burial [BEHR ee uhl] having to do with placing a body in its final resting place

C

carnage [KAHR nij] killing of a great number of people or animals

cello [CHEL oh] a musical instrument like a violin, but much larger, that is played in a sitting position

challenge [CHAL unj] a call to a contest or battle

chant [CHANT] rapid and rhythmic speaking

chasms [KAZ umz] deep openings or cracks

clamor [KLAM ur] demand noisily; loudly call for

classification [klas ih fih KAY shun] putting something into a special group or class

commend [kuh MEND] praise; acclaim as worthy of notice

compete [kom PEET] oppose; try for the same thing

conductor [kuhn DUK tuhr] the leader of a group of musicians

conservationists [kon sur VAY shu nists] persons who wish to save forms of animals and plant life in danger of being destroyed forever

considerable [kun SID ur uh bul] not a little; much

contract [KON trakt] a legal paper promising a job

cradle [KRAY dul] a framework upon which a ship rests, usually during repair

cremated [KREE mayt id] burnt to ashes

crescent [KRES unt] the shape of the moon in the first or last quarter; the symbol of the Muslim religion

cuisine [kwih ZEEN] style of cooking

cultural [Kul chur ul] relating to art, good taste, and education

D

debut [DAY byoo] a first appearance before the public

definitely [DEF uh nit lee] absolutely

denote [dih NOHT] show; point out

devoted [dee VOH tid] gave up one's time, money, or efforts for some cause or person

dictatorship [dik TAY tur ship] rule by one person or group that must be obeyed; power held by a few through force

diminutive [duh MIN yoo tiv] very small, tiny

disciplinarian [dis uh plih NEHR ee uhn] a person who believes in strict training

documentary [dok yuh MEN tuh ree] factual presentation of a scene, place, or condition of life in writing or on film

dwindled [DWIN duld] reduced in number

E

eclipses [ee KLIP siz] times when the sun or moon cannot be seen because its light is blocked

efforts [EF furts] attempts

elaborate [ih LAB or uht] complicated; intricate

embodies [em BOD eez] to represent in real or definite form

endure [en DYOOR] last; keep on

enforce [en FORS] make someone do something; compel

enthusiastic [en THOO zee AS tik] eagerly interested

erupt [ee RUPT] explode; burst forth

essence [ES uns] that which makes something what it is

essential [ee SEN chul] very important

exert [eg ZURT] apply; full use

exhibited [eks ZIH bih tid] displayed; shown to the public

expedition [ek spuh DISH un] group of people

undertaking a special journey, such as mountain climbing

experience *[ek SPIR ee uns]* active participation in events

explanation *[ek spluh NAY shun]* a statement that clears up a difficulty or mistake

exposition *[ek spuh ZISH un]* public show or exhibition

expressions *[ek SPRESH unz]* sounds or actions which show some feelings

extemporized *[ek STEM puh ryzd]* performed without preparation

extermination *[ek STUR muh NAY shun]* the act of destroying completely; putting an end to

F

fan *[FAN]* enthusiastic supporter

fare *[FAIR]* cost of a ticket

fascinated *[FAS uh nay tid]* amazed; very interested by

festivals *[FES tuh vulz]* celebrations

fiction *[FIK shun]* a story that is not true

flawless *[FLAW les]* perfect; without fault

forebears *[FOR behrz]* family members who lived a long time ago

frantic *[FRAN tik]* wild with excitement; out of control

frolic *[FRO lik]* to play about happily

G

gingerly *[JIN jur lee]* very carefully

gloss *[GLOS]* high polish; shine

gourmets *[goor MAYZ]* people who like and know about good food

grave *[GRAYV]* serious; critical

H

hardy *[HAHR dee]* able to take hard physical treatment; bold; daring

harpoon *[hahr POON]* a long spear with a rope tied to it used in killing a whale

hindrances *[HIN drun siz]* things that block a goal

hoax *[HOKS]* a trick

homeland *[HOHM land]* place of origin

humble *[HUM bul]* lowly

humid *[HYOO mid]* damp, moist air

I

identify *[i DEN tuh fy]* recognize as being a particular person or thing

ignorance *[IG nur uns]* lack of knowledge

impressionistic *[im preh shun IS tik]* in the style of painting in which the painter tries to catch a momentary glimpse of the subject

influence *[IN floo ins]* motivating force

intent *[in TENT]* concentrating; paying close attention

interior *[in TEER ee ur]* inside; inner part

investigate *[in VES tih gayt]* study; look into carefully

issues *[ISH yooz]* topics or problems under discussion

J

jointly *[JOINT lee]* together; in partnership

L

laden *[LAY din]* loaded; heavily burdened

landmark *[LAND mark]* something familiar or easily seen

lava *[LAH vuh]* melted rock that comes from a volcano

literacy *[LIT ur uh see]* ability to read and write

M

mammals *[MAM ulz]* animals that feed milk to their young; people belong to this group

manager *[MAN ij ur]* a performer's business arranger

matter *[MAT ur]* a real thing; content rather than manner or style

métier *[may TYAY]* life's work; occupation; profession

mingle *[MING gul]* mix; get along together

mission *[MIH shun]* a special task

monarch *[MON ahrk]* king or queen; an absolute ruler

monument *[MON yuh munt]* something from a past age that is believed to have historical importance

motivated *[MOH tuh vayt id]* stimulated to do something; inspired

N

notable *[NOH tuh bul]* worthy of notice; remarkable

novels *[NOV uls]* long stories about imaginary people and events

O

obscure *[ub SKYOOR]* unnoticed; undistinguished

opposition *[op uh ZISH un]* group against the government in power

orchestra *[OR kes truh]* musicians who perform together, especially on stringed instruments

organic *[or GAN ik]* grown without synthetic substances

ornamented *[OR nuh men tid]* decorated; made more beautiful

ovations *[oh VAY shunz]* burst of loud clapping or cheering; waves of applause

P

pagan *[PAY gun]* a follower of a religion with many gods

panorama *[pan uh RAM uh]* a wide view of a surrounding region

partakes *[pahr TAYKS]* shares

peak *[PEEK]* the top; the highest point

pedigree *[PED ih gree]* record of an animal's ancestors, especially with respect to purity of breed

perilous *[PEHR uh lus]* dangerous; hazardous

perished *[PEHR isht]* died, usually in a violent manner

permanent *[PUR muh nunt]* lasting; continuing

perplex *[pur PLEKS]* puzzle; confuse

petition *[puh TISH un]* a written document of request

plantation *[plan TAY shun]* large estate or farm

plastic *[PLAS tik]* a synthetic or processed material

platform *[PLAT form]* a raised level surface

plight *[PLYT]* condition or state, usually bad

popularize *[POP yoo lar yz]* makes popular

preferable *[PREH fir uh bul]* something liked better; more desirable

primitive *[PRIM uh tiv]* living long ago; from earliest times

privileged *[PRIV lijd]* having advantages

prodigy *[PROD uh jee]* a highly gifted or talented person, usually a child

produce *[PROH doos]* fresh fruits and vegetables

products *[PROD ukts]* manufactured items

profession *[pruh FESH un]* an occupation requiring an education

project *[PRO jekt]* an undertaking, often a big, complicated job

proof *[PROOF]* facts; evidence

prosperous *[PROS per us]* successful

protest *[PROH test]* strong objection; opposition

pundits *[PUN ditz]* persons who have great knowledge of a subject

pursuing *[pur SOO ing]* striving for

R

racial *[RAY shul]* of, or having to do with race or origins

recently *[REE sint lee]* a short time ago; lately

recognized *[REK ug NYZD]* identified

reflect *[ree FLEKT]* give back an image of

religious *[ree LIJ us]* having to do with a belief in God; devout

renditions *[ren DISH uns]* performances or interpretations

renowned *[rih NOUND]* having a great reputation; famous

reputable *[REP yuh tuh bul]* honorable; well thought of

resembles *[ree ZEM bulz]* looks like; similar in appearance

restored *[rih STORD]* brought back to its original state; reconstructed

restricted *[ree STRIKT id]* limited in freedom or use

retrospective *[RET ruh SPEK TIV]* an exhibition of the life-time work of an artist

romanticist *[roh MAN tih sist]* one who paints people and things as she or he would like them to be rather than as they really are

rural *[RUR ul]* having to do with open country and farming

S

sacred *[SAY krid]* holy; worthy of reverence

salvage *[SAL vij]* the act of saving a ship or its cargo from the sea

scale *[SKAYL]* climb

scholarship *[SKOL ur ship]* money given to help a student pay for studies

script *[SKRIPT]* written text of a play or movie

segregation *[seg ruh GAY shun]* separation from others; setting individuals or groups apart from society

sheer *[SHEER]* steep; straight up and down

shrines *[SHRYNZ]* sacred places; places where holy things are kept

shy *[SHY]* modest, uncertain

sire *[SYR]* be the father of

skeptical *[SKEP tuh kul]* having doubts; not willing to believe

skillful *[SKIL ful]* having ability gained by practice or knowledge; expert

smart *[SMAHRT]* feel a sharp pain; sting

soared *[SOHRD]* rose upward quickly

souvenirs *[SOO vuh NEERS]* things bought or kept for remembrance

spectacular *[spek TAK yuh lur]* eye-catching; very unusual

spurs *[SPURZ]* urges on; encourages

structures *[STRUK churz]* things that are built, such as buildings or towers

stunned *[STUND]* made senseless, dizzy; confused

summit *[SUM it]* peak; highest point

symbols *[SIM bulz]* things that stand for or represent something else; signs

synonymous *[si NON uh mus]* alike in meaning or significance

T

talent *[TAL unt]* a natural gift for doing something

taste *[TAYST]* a sense of what is good

toast *[TOHST]* a popular and admired person

trade *[TRAYD]* job; skill

tremendous *[truh MEN dus]* huge; enormous

turmoil *[TUR moil]* confusion; commotion

tyranny *[TIR uh nee]* cruel use of power

U

unaffected *[UN uh FEK tid]* not influenced or changed; natural

urged *[URJD]* advised strongly

V

vanish *[VAN ish]* disappear

vast *[VAST]* huge; spacious

volcano *[vol KAY noh]* a mountain with a cuplike crater which throws out hot melted rock and steam

vulnerable *[VUL nur uh bul]* defenseless against; open to attack or injury